ORIGO
STEPPING STONES 2.0
COMPREHENSIVE MATHEMATICS

AUTHORS

James Burnett
Calvin Irons
Peter Stowasser
Allan Turton

PROGRAM CONSULTANTS

Diana Lambdin
Frank Lester, Jr.
Kit Norris

CONTRIBUTING WRITERS

Donna Arnott   Beth Lewis
Jaye Kelly   Melanie Theed

STUDENT BOOK B

ORIGO
EDUCATION

CONTENTS

© ORIGO Education

ORIGO Stepping Stones • Grade 1

CONTENTS

ORIGO Stepping Stones • Grade 1

Step In   What do you know about one hundred?

There are 100 cents in one dollar.

I have seen 100 miles on signs.

Where have you seen **100** written?

How would you write 100 on this expander?

Write **100** on this expander. What do you notice?

Write **100** on this expander. What do you notice?

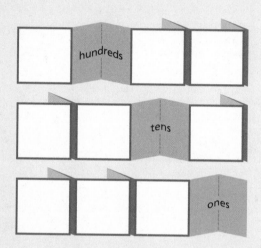

Step Up   1. Use the number chart to help you answer the questions.

61	62	63	64	65	66	67	68	69	70
71	72	73	74	75	76	77	78	79	80
81	82	83	84	85	86	87	88	89	90
91	92	93	94	95	96	97	98	99	100

a. What number is **one less** than 100? ☐

b. What number is **ten less** than 100? ☐

2. Circle the number. Then write the number of ones left over.

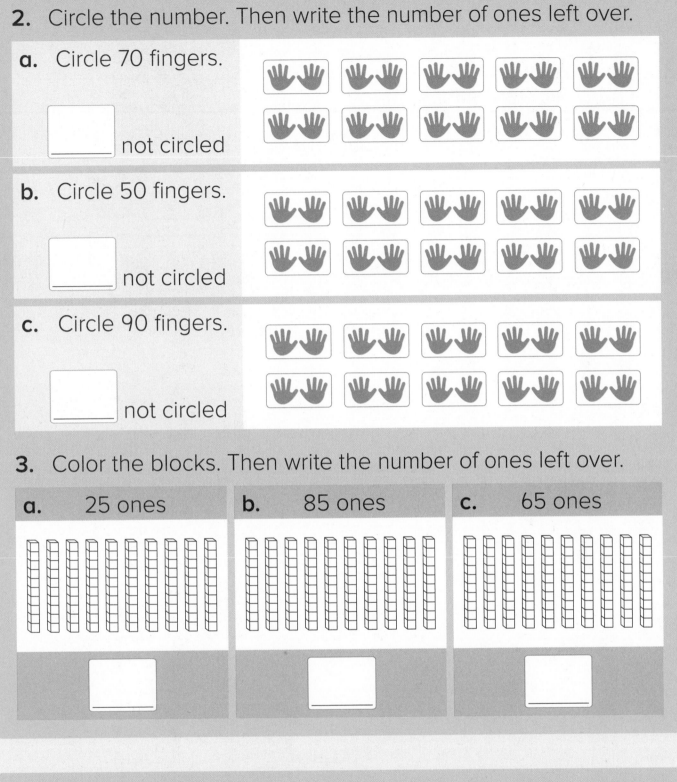

a. Circle 70 fingers.

[ ] not circled

b. Circle 50 fingers.

[ ] not circled

c. Circle 90 fingers.

[ ] not circled

3. Color the blocks. Then write the number of ones left over.

a. 25 ones

b. 85 ones

c. 65 ones

Step Ahead — Complete these to show other pairs of two-digit numbers that make 100.

a. [ ] 0 and [ ] 0

b. [ ] 5 and [ ] 5

c. [ ] 5 and [ ] 5

Step In **What number does this picture of blocks show?**

How would you write this number on an expander? How do you know?

hundreds   tens   ones

Look at the number on this expander. What does each digit mean?

| 1 | hundreds | 1 | tens | 0 | ones |

How is this number different from the number on the first expander above?

Step Up **I.** Look at the blocks.
Write the number on the expanders to match.

a.

b.

c.

2. Color the blocks to match the number shown
on each expander.

a.

| 1 | hundreds | 0 | 5 |

b.

| 1 | hundreds | 0 | 2 |

c.

| 1 | hundreds | 0 | 8 |

d.

| 1 | hundreds | 1 | 0 |

Step Ahead Draw more blocks to match the number
on the expander.

| 1 | hundreds | 0 | 9 |

Computation Practice

★ Complete the equations as fast as you can.

start

$8 + 8 =$ ☐

$5 + 3 =$ ☐

$2 + 6 =$ ☐

$2 + 8 =$ ☐

$5 - 2 =$ ☐

$4 + 4 =$ ☐

$3 + 3 =$ ☐

$6 + 1 =$ ☐

$4 - 3 =$ ☐

$7 + 7 =$ ☐

$8 + 1 =$ ☐

$2 + 3 =$ ☐

$5 + 6 =$ ☐

$3 + 4 =$ ☐

$5 - 4 =$ ☐

$5 + 5 =$ ☐

$1 + 4 =$ ☐

$4 - 2 =$ ☐

$8 + 7 =$ ☐

$6 + 6 =$ ☐

finish

Ongoing Practice **1.** Write the number in each part and the total.

One part is ____.

The other part is ____.

The total is ____.

2. a. Write **100** on each expander.

hundreds   tens   ones

b. How many ones equal 100?

c. How many tens equal 100?

d. How many hundreds equal 100?

Preparing for Module 8   Draw more dots to make 10.
Then complete the matching equation.

a.

____ + ____ = 10

b.

____ + ____ = 10

Step In

How would you read and say the number on this expander?

Do you have to say the number of tens?

How would you write the number in words?

How would you read and say these numbers?

What does the zero in each number tell you?

Step Up

1. Look at the blocks. Write the number on the expanders. Then write the matching number name.

a.

_____ hundred _____

b.

_____ hundred _____

2. Read the number name. Write the matching number on the expander.

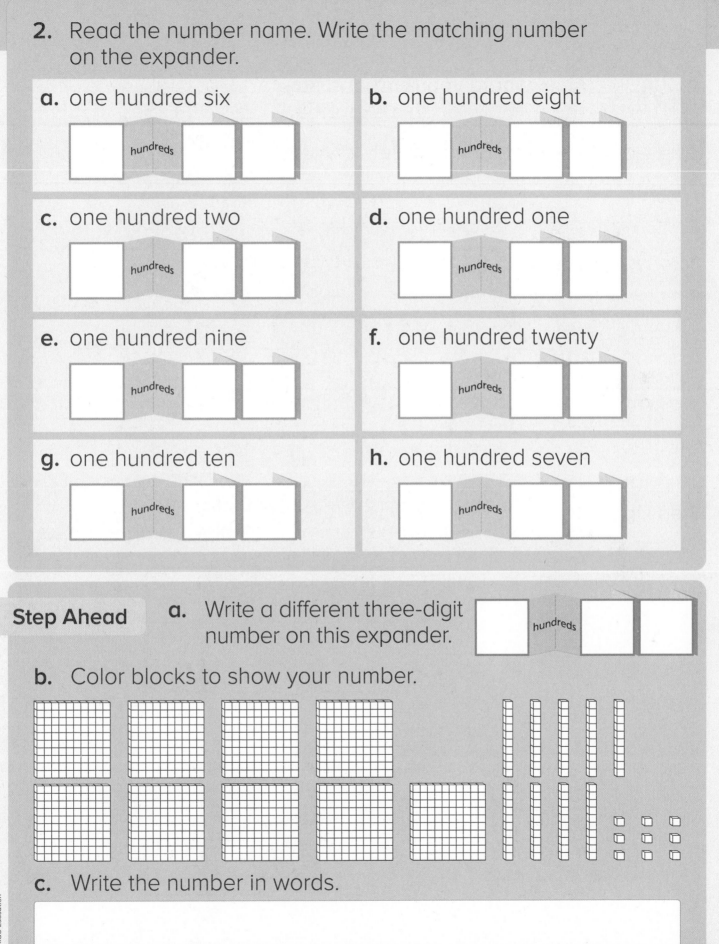

a. one hundred six

| | hundreds | | |

b. one hundred eight

| | hundreds | | |

c. one hundred two

| | hundreds | | |

d. one hundred one

| | hundreds | | |

e. one hundred nine

| | hundreds | | |

f. one hundred twenty

| | hundreds | | |

g. one hundred ten

| | hundreds | | |

h. one hundred seven

| | hundreds | | |

Step Ahead

a. Write a different three-digit number on this expander.

| | hundreds | | |

b. Color blocks to show your number.

c. Write the number in words.

Step In   How would you read and say the number on this expander?

1 hundreds 1 6

How would you write the number in words?

_____

How would you read and say these two numbers?

1 hundreds 0 4   1 hundreds 1 4

What is the same about these numbers?
What is different?

Step Up   1. Look at the blocks. Write the number on the expanders. Then write the matching number name.

a.

hundreds   tens   ones

hundreds

_____ hundred _____

b.

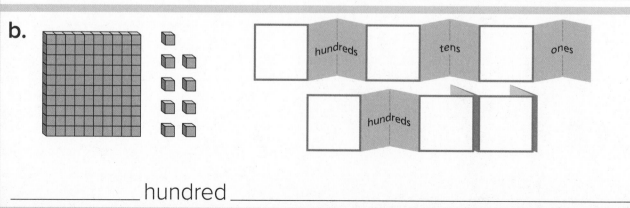

hundreds   tens   ones

hundreds

_____ hundred _____

2. Read the number name. Write the matching number on the expander.

a. one hundred thirteen

| | hundreds | | |

b. one hundred eight

| | hundreds | | |

c. one hundred eleven

| | hundreds | | |

d. one hundred eighteen

| | hundreds | | |

e. one hundred seventeen

| | hundreds | | |

f. one hundred seven

| | hundreds | | |

g. one hundred twenty

| | hundreds | | |

h. one hundred twelve

| | hundreds | | |

Step Ahead   Read this number.

| 1 | hundreds | 0 | 2 |

a. Color blocks to show a number that is **10 greater**.

b. Write the number that is greater in words.

Think and Solve The same shapes are the same number. Write the missing number inside each square to complete the equation.

$$\Box + \Box = 9 - \Box$$

Words at Work

a. Write about where you have seen 100.

b. Draw a picture to show what you saw.

Ongoing Practice

I. Complete the addition fact to figure out the number of carrots that were taken. Then complete the subtraction fact to match.

a.

$6 + \boxed{} = 7$

$7 - 6 = \boxed{}$

b.

$5 + \boxed{} = 8$

$8 - 5 = \boxed{}$

2. Look at the blocks. Write the matching number on the expanders.

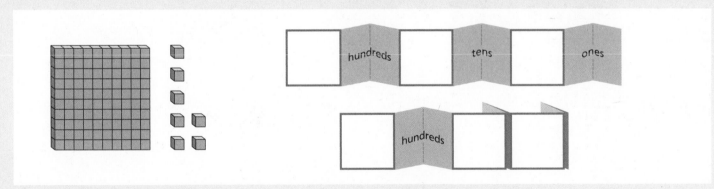

hundreds   tens   ones

hundreds

Preparing for Module 8

Draw more dots to make 10.
Then complete the matching equation.

a.

$\boxed{} + \boxed{} = 10$

b.

$\boxed{} + \boxed{} = 10$

Step In

How do you read and say the number on this expander?

| 1 | hundreds | 0 | tens | 7 | ones |

What blocks would you use to show the number?

How could you use this place-value chart to show the number?

Hundreds	Tens	Ones

How would you write the numeral without using an expander or a place-value chart?

Step Up

1. Look at each picture of blocks. Write the number of hundreds, tens, and ones.

a.

Hundreds	Tens	Ones

b.

Hundreds	Tens	Ones

c.

Hundreds	Tens	Ones

d.

Hundreds	Tens	Ones

2. Look at each picture of blocks. Write the matching number in the place-value chart. Then write the numeral without the chart.

a.

Hundreds	Tens	Ones

b.

Hundreds	Tens	Ones

c.

Hundreds	Tens	Ones

d.

Hundreds	Tens	Ones

e.

Hundreds	Tens	Ones

Step Ahead   Draw **another tens block and a ones block** in each picture. Write the numeral to match the new picture.

a.

b.

Step In

Color blocks to match the numeral.
Then write the number name.

112

_____ hundred _____

How would you write the numeral to show
the number of blocks that you did not color?

How would you write the number in words?

Step Up

1. Look at each picture of blocks. Write the matching
number in the place-value chart. Then write
the numeral without the chart.

a.

Hundreds	Tens	Ones

b.

Hundreds	Tens	Ones

c.

Hundreds	Tens	Ones

© ORIGO Education

2. Write the numeral and number name to match the blocks.

a.

b.

c.

3. Write the numeral to match each number name.

a. one hundred fifteen

b. thirty

c. one hundred one

Step Ahead   Write the numeral to match this picture of blocks.

Computation Practice   **Why did the teacher wear dark glasses?**

★ Complete the equations.

★ Write each letter above its matching total at the bottom of the page. Some letters are used more than once.

□ = 7 + 5	u	□ = 2 + 8	r
□ = 8 + 9	c	□ = 3 + 4	d
□ = 4 + 1	g	□ = 6 + 7	e
□ = 2 + 2	a	□ = 9 + 9	h
□ = 9 + 7	b	□ = 7 + 2	t
□ = 2 + 6	i	□ = 8 + 6	s

16 13 17 4 12 14 13   14 18 13

18 4 7   14 12 17 18   4

16 10 8 5 18 9   17   I   4 14 14

© ORIGO Education

1. Figure out the number of dots that are covered. Then complete the facts.

a.

$8 - 4 = \boxed{}$

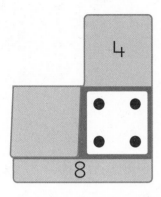

$4 + \boxed{} = 8$

b.

$12 - 6 = \boxed{}$

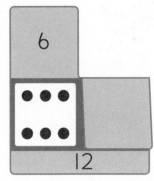

$6 + \boxed{} = 12$

c.

$16 - 8 = \boxed{}$

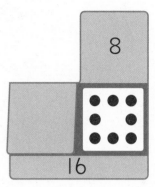

$8 + \boxed{} = 16$

2. Read the number name. Write the matching number on the expander.

a. one hundred three

b. one hundred eighteen

Preparing for Module 8   Write two equations to match each domino.

a.

$\boxed{} + \boxed{} = \boxed{}$

$\boxed{} + \boxed{} = \boxed{}$

b.

$\boxed{} + \boxed{} = \boxed{}$

$\boxed{} + \boxed{} = \boxed{}$

Step In   This train has seven cars. Some of the cars are already in the tunnel.

How many cars are in the tunnel? How do you know?

I can think addition to figure out the answer. That is 3 + ___ = 7.

Which doubles fact could you use to help figure out the answer?

Write the missing numbers.

3	+	3	=	6
___	+	___	=	7
4	+	4	=	8

Step Up   I.   Write the missing number and draw the matching dots on each card. Then complete the addition facts.

a.

4 + ☐ = 9

b.

☐ + 5 = 12

c.

6 + ☐ = 13

2. Figure out the number of dots that are covered.
Then complete the facts.

a. $10 - 4 =$ ☐

$4 +$ ☐ $= 10$

b. $11 - 5 =$ ☐

$5 +$ ☐ $= 11$

c. $8 - 3 =$ ☐

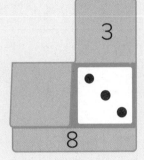

$3 +$ ☐ $= 8$

d. $15 - 7 =$ ☐

$7 +$ ☐ $= 15$

e. $16 - 9 =$ ☐

$9 +$ ☐ $= 16$

f. $14 - 6 =$ ☐

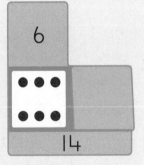

$6 +$ ☐ $= 14$

Step Ahead Write a doubles fact that you could use to solve the problem. Then write the answer.

Kimie bakes 13 muffins. She gives 6 muffins away and stores the rest in a container.

☐ $+$ ☐ $=$ ☐

How many muffins are in the container? ☐ muffins

Step In

There are 12 eggs in a carton. Then some eggs are cooked for breakfast. There are now 5 eggs left.

How many eggs were cooked at breakfast?

What doubles fact could you use to help figure out the answer?

I will think addition. That is 5 + ___ = 12.
I know double 5 is 10 and 2 more is 12.
So 5 add 7 is 12.

How can you use the same thinking to figure out 11 − 6?

What doubles fact could you use?

This time I will double 6 and then take one away.

Step Up

1. Draw dots to figure out the missing part. Then complete the addition and subtraction facts to match.

a. 13 dots in total

13 − 6 = ☐

think

6 + ☐ = 13

b. 9 dots in total

9 − 4 = ☐

think

4 + ☐ = 9

2. Figure out the number of dots that are covered.
Then complete the facts.

a. 8 dots in total

8 − 3 = ◻

3 + ◻ = 8

b. 15 dots in total

15 − 8 = ◻

8 + ◻ = 15

c. 14 dots in total

14 − 6 = ◻

6 + ◻ = 14

d. 16 dots in total

16 − 7 = ◻

7 + ◻ = 16

e. 7 dots in total

7 − 3 = ◻

3 + ◻ = 7

f. 17 dots in total

17 − 8 = ◻

8 + ◻ = 17

3. Write each answer.

a. 5 − 2 = ◻

b. 11 − 5 = ◻

c. 10 − 4 = ◻

Step Ahead Write the addition fact you would use to figure out
each answer. Then complete the subtraction facts.

a. 12 − 5 = ◻

b. 9 − 7 = ◻

c. 8 − 6 = ◻

_____

_____

_____

Think and Solve

Susan is 8 years old.

Jerome is 3 years older than Susan.

Jerome and Amy are the same age.

a. How old is Jerome? _____

b. How old is Amy? _____

Words at Work Choose and write a word from the list to complete each sentence. Some words from the list are not used.

> thirteen
> eighty
> ones
> place value
> expander
> tens
> hundred

a. _____ is the same value as 8 tens.

b. One less than one _____ is 99.

c. An _____ is used to show the number of hundreds, tens, and ones in a number.

d. The number name for 113 is one hundred _____.

e. 102 has one hundred, zero _____, and two _____.

Ongoing Practice

I. Color **one** part of each picture red. Then circle each picture that shows **one-half** in red.

a.

b.

c.

d.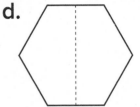

2. Figure out the number of dots that are covered. Then complete the facts.

a.
$$9 - 4 = \boxed{}$$

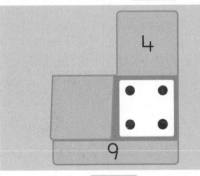

$$4 + \boxed{} = 9$$

b.
$$11 - 6 = \boxed{}$$

$$6 + \boxed{} = 11$$

c.
$$8 - 5 = \boxed{}$$

$$5 + \boxed{} = 8$$

Preparing for Module 8

Draw ◯ in each empty box to make each balance picture true. Then complete the equation to match.

a.

$$\boxed{} \text{ and } \boxed{} = \boxed{}$$

b.

$$\boxed{} = \boxed{} \text{ and } \boxed{}$$

Step In Solve each problem.

9 toys are on a shelf.
Then 2 toys are sold.
How many toys are left?

11 apples are in a bowl.
Then some of the apples are
eaten. There are 5 apples left.
How many apples were eaten?

7 friends are playing at the
pool. 5 friends are in the
water. The other friends are
out of the water. How many
friends are out of the water?

15 passengers are on a bus.
8 passengers get off the
bus. How many passengers
are left on the bus?

Think about the strategy you used to solve each problem.

Write **C** on the problem if you used count-back.
Write **A** on the problem if you used think-addition.
Write **D** on the problem if you used use-doubles.

Which problems could you solve by thinking about addition
and using a double?

Step Up   I.   Write the answers. Then write **A** beside
the equations that you solved by thinking
about addition.

a.
$8 - 1 =$ ☐

b.
$5 - 3 =$ ☐

c.
$7 - 6 =$ ☐

d.
$10 - 2 =$ ☐

e.
$12 - 6 =$ ☐

f.
$9 - 4 =$ ☐

2. Solve each problem. Show your thinking.

a. There are 15 flowers in a vase. 7 flowers are red. The rest are purple. How many flowers are purple?

_____ flowers

b. 8 birds are sitting on a fence. 2 birds fly away. How many birds are now on the fence?

_____ birds

c. There are 16 mice in a cage. Some run out. 7 mice are now in the cage. How many ran out?

_____ mice

d. Cooper runs 5 laps on a track. He wants to run 8 laps. How many more laps does he need to run?

_____ laps

Step Ahead   Write numbers to make this word story true.

_____ puppies are playing by a fence. _____ puppies run away.

There are now _____ puppies playing by the fence.

Step In	Look at this analog clock.

The short hand counts the hours
and the long hand counts the minutes.

What time is this clock showing?
How do you know?

How long does it take the minute hand
to make one full turn around the clock?

**Where would the minute hand point
if it went halfway around?**

When the minute hand is pointing at 6,
it is **half-past** an hour.

When the minute hand shows a half-past time,
what does the hour hand show?

What time is this clock showing? How do you know?

Step Up	I. Write the time showing on each clock.

a.

half-past

____ o'clock

b.

half-past

____ o'clock

c.

half-past

____ o'clock

2. Write each time in words.

a.

b.

c.

_____

_____

_____

d.

e.

f.

_____

_____

_____

Step Ahead Circle the clocks that show times **between** half-past 7 and 10 o'clock.

Computation Practice

★ Complete the equations.

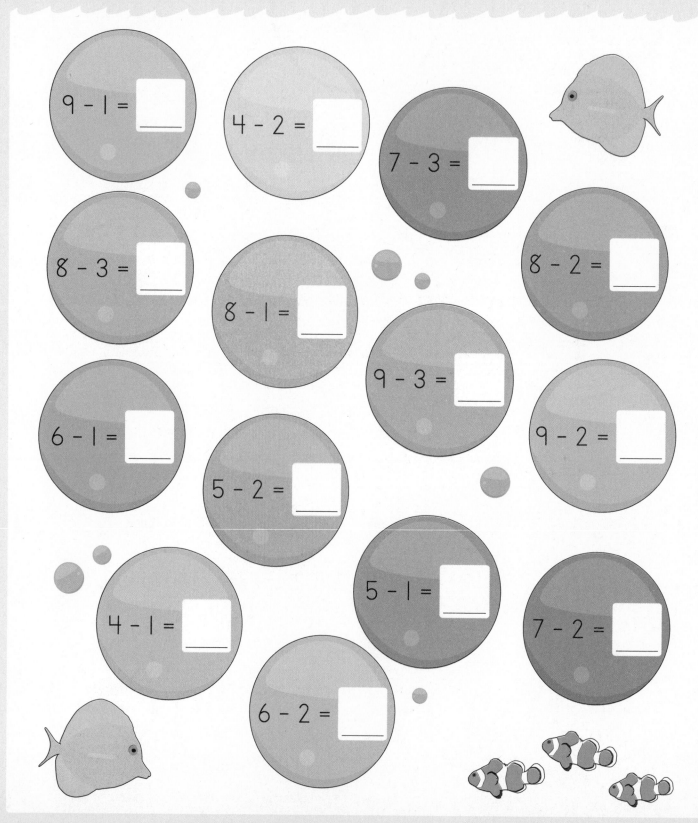

9 − 1 = ☐

4 − 2 = ☐

7 − 3 = ☐

8 − 3 = ☐

8 − 1 = ☐

8 − 2 = ☐

6 − 1 = ☐

9 − 3 = ☐

9 − 2 = ☐

5 − 2 = ☐

4 − 1 = ☐

5 − 1 = ☐

7 − 2 = ☐

6 − 2 = ☐

I. Color **one** part of each strip red. Then circle the strip that shows **one-fourth** in red.

a.

b.

c.

2. Solve each problem. Show your thinking.

a. There are 11 puppies in a pet store. Then 3 puppies are sold. How many are left in the store?

_____ puppies

b. James has 15 pennies. He spends some pennies and has 12 pennies left. How many pennies did he spend?

_____ pennies

Preparing for Module 8   Some students voted for their favorite pet.

Draw a ✔ beside each animal to show each vote.

2 students voted for fish.
3 students voted for birds.
6 students voted for dogs.

🐦	
🐟	
🐕	

Step In How many minutes are in one hour?

How many minutes are in half an hour? How do you know?

Look at this digital clock.

How is this clock different from an analog clock?

What do you know about the time on this clock?

> The 30 shows me the number of minutes. I know it is a half-past time because 30 minutes is half of one hour.

What time is the clock showing?

Step Up 1. Draw a line from each label to a matching clock. Some clocks do not have a match.

2. Write each time in words.

a. _____

b. _____

c. _____

d. _____

e. _____

f. _____

g. _____

Step Ahead   Complete the sentences.

a.

The time is half-past _____ ☐.
One hour **later** will be half-past _____ ☐.

b.

The time is half-past _____ ☐.
One hour **later** will be half-past _____ ☐.

Step In

What different ways can you say the time shown on these clocks?

Half-past three.

Three thirty.

Step Up

1. Write each time on the digital clock.

a.

:

b.

:

c.

:

d.

:

e.

:

f.

:

2. Draw lines to connect matching times.

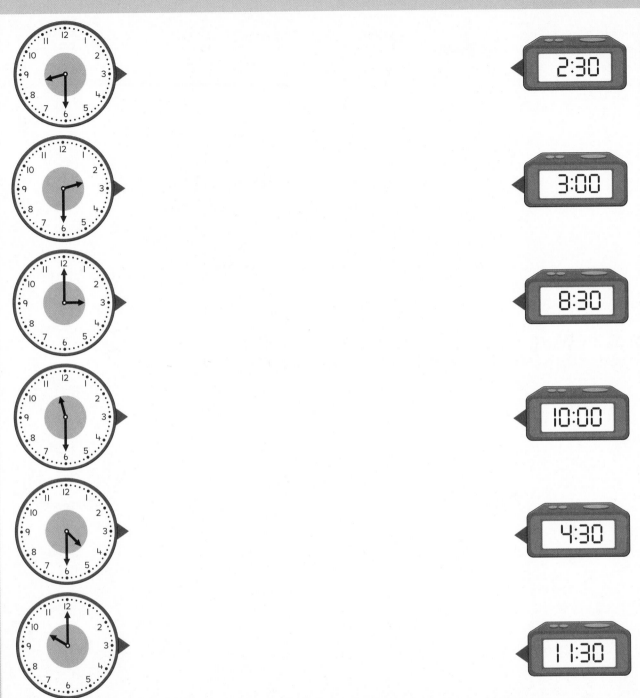

Step Ahead

Gemma has breakfast at 7:00 on Monday morning. She has baseball practice at 4:00 in the afternoon.

How many half-past the hour times will there be on the clock between breakfast and the start of baseball practice?

Think and Solve The same shapes weigh the same.
Write the missing value inside each shape.

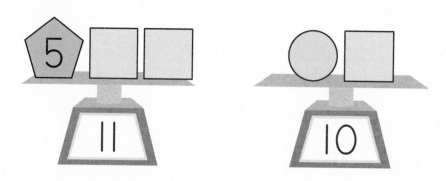

Words at Work Write about this clock. You can use words from the list to help.

| time |
| counts |
| minutes |
| minute hand |
| hour hand |
| half-past |
| hour |
| analog |
| digital |

Ongoing Practice

1. For each strip, write the fraction that is purple.

a.

b.

2. Write the time shown on each clock.

a.
half-past ___ o'clock

b.
half-past ___ o'clock

c.
half-past ___ o'clock

Preparing for Module 8

Draw tally marks on the chart to show the votes.

8 students voted yes.
6 students voted no.

Do you like vegetables?	
Yes	
No	

What number am I?

I have more ones than tens.

I have an odd number of ones.

I have a one in the hundreds place.

Evan says it will be lunchtime in 30 minutes.

Lunchtime is at 1 o'clock.

Do you agree with Evan? Show your thinking.

Ask for feedback. Share how the feedback helps you.

Step In   Look at these cubes.

What addition fact matches the picture?

How else could you break up the cubes?

What other addition facts could you write?

Step Up   1. Color some of the cubes.
Then write a matching addition fact.

a.

☐ + ☐ = 10

b.

☐ + ☐ = 10

c.

☐ + ☐ = 10

2. Use different colors to show three parts.
Then write a matching equation.

a.

$\boxed{} + \boxed{} + \boxed{} = \boxed{10}$

b.

$\boxed{} + \boxed{} + \boxed{} = \boxed{}$

c.

$\boxed{} + \boxed{} + \boxed{} = \boxed{}$

d.

$\boxed{} + \boxed{} + \boxed{} = \boxed{}$

Step Ahead Think of some different ways to break up **11** cubes.
Then complete these equations to match.

$\boxed{} + \boxed{} = \boxed{11}$ $\boxed{11} = \boxed{} + \boxed{}$

$\boxed{} + \boxed{} + \boxed{} = \boxed{11}$ $\boxed{11} = \boxed{} + \boxed{} + \boxed{}$

Addition: Using the associative property

Step In   How many bugs are on each leaf?

How would you figure out the total number of bugs?

In what order did you decide to add the number of bugs on each leaf?

I looked for two numbers that make 10. I then added the last number.

Write an equation to show the order that you decided to add.

☐ + ☐ + ☐ = ☐

Does the total change if you add them in a different order?

Step Up   I.   Draw ⌢ to show two groups that make 10. Write an equation to show how you add to find the total.

a.

☐ + ☐ + ☐ = ☐

b.

☐ + ☐ + ☐ = ☐

c.

☐ + ☐ + ☐ = ☐

d.

☐ + ☐ + ☐ = ☐

2. Draw ⌢ to show two numbers that make 10. Then write an equation to show how you add to find the total.

a.

☐ + ☐ + ☐ = ☐

b.

☐ + ☐ + ☐ = ☐

c.

☐ + ☐ + ☐ = ☐

d.

☐ + ☐ + ☐ = ☐

e.

☐ + ☐ + ☐ = ☐

f.

☐ + ☐ + ☐ = ☐

Step Ahead Write three different equations to match this picture.

☐ + ☐ + ☐ = ☐

☐ + ☐ + ☐ = ☐

☐ + ☐ + ☐ = ☐

Computation Practice

★ Complete the equations.

★ Draw a line to join each light and switch that have matching totals.

$8 + 6 =$

$9 + 3 =$

$7 + 6 =$

$6 + 5 =$

$12 + 3 =$

| $7 + 7$ | $3 + 8$ | $7 + 8$ | $11 + 2$ | $5 + 7$ |

I. Color blocks to show the number of ones.
Then write the number of ones left over.

FROM 1.7.1

a. 30 ones **b.** 90 ones **c.** 50 ones

2. Use different colors to show two or three parts.
Then write the matching equation.

FROM 1.8.1

a.

☐ + ☐ = 10

b.

☐ + ☐ + ☐ = ☐

Preparing for Module 9

Draw jumps to help you count on.
Write two addition facts to match.

Count on **2**.

| 11 | 12 | 13 | 14 | 15 | 16 | 17 | 18 | 19 | 20 |

☐ + ☐ = ☐

☐ + ☐ = ☐

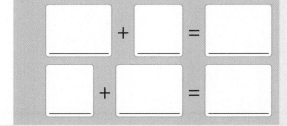

Addition: Introducing the make-ten strategy

Step In Look at this picture of counters.

How can you figure out the total?

I moved one counter to make a group of 10. This made it easier to add.

9 + 3
is the same value as 10 + 2.
10 + 2 is 12.

How would you use this strategy to figure out 9 + 6?

Step Up

1. Draw more counters. Then write the numbers to match.

a. Draw 5 more.

see ➤ 9 + 5

think ➤ 10 + 4

b. Draw 3 more.

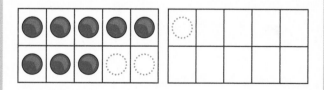

see ➤ ☐ + ☐

think ➤ ☐ + ☐

2. Draw more counters. Then write the numbers to match.

a. Draw 6 more.

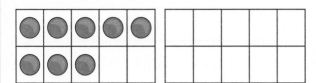

see ▶ ☐ + ☐

think ▶ ☐ + ☐

b. Draw 7 more.

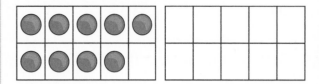

see ▶ ☐ + ☐

think ▶ ☐ + ☐

c. Draw 4 more.

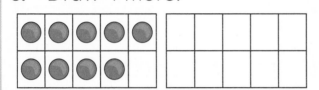

see ▶ ☐ + ☐

think ▶ ☐ + ☐

d. Draw 5 more.

see ▶ ☐ + ☐

think ▶ ☐ + ☐

Step Ahead | Think of **six** different ways this cube train could be broken into two groups. Complete the equations to match.

☐ + ☐ = ☐   ☐ + ☐ = ☐

☐ + ☐ = ☐   ☐ + ☐ = ☐

☐ + ☐ = ☐   ☐ + ☐ = ☐

Step In **Look at this picture of counters.**

How many counters are **on** the ten-frame?
How many counters are **off** the ten-frame?

How could you use the ten-frame to figure out the total?

I could move two counters to fill the ten-frame.

Circle the box below that matches the thinking above.

8 + 5	8 + 5	8 + 5
is the same value as	is the same value as	is the same value as
10 + 2	10 + 5	10 + 3

How could you use a ten-frame to figure out 9 + 4?

Step Up **1.** Draw more counters to figure out the total. Fill the ten-frame first. Then write the tens fact to match the picture.

a. 9 + 3 = ☐

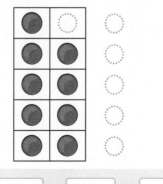

10 + ☐ = ☐

b. 9 + 6 = ☐

10 + ☐ = ☐

c. 8 + 4 = ☐

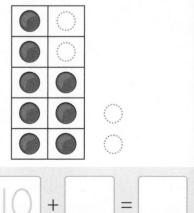

10 + ☐ = ☐

2. Draw more counters to figure out the total. Fill the ten-frame first. Then write the tens fact to match the picture.

a.
9 + 5 = ☐

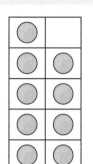

☐ + ☐ = ☐

b.
7 + 5 = ☐

☐ + ☐ = ☐

c.
9 + 7 = ☐

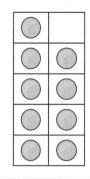

☐ + ☐ = ☐

d.
8 + 7 = ☐

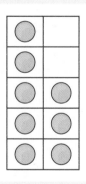

☐ + ☐ = ☐

e.
9 + 8 = ☐

☐ + ☐ = ☐

f.
8 + 3 = ☐

☐ + ☐ = ☐

Step Ahead   Circle the facts that have the same total as the counters in this picture.

9 + 3   8 + 5   7 + 5

8 + 4   8 + 3

Think and Solve

Imagine you can only move ⟶ or ↑.

•⟶ is 1 unit.

How many units will be in
the **shortest** path from **A** to **B**? [   ] units

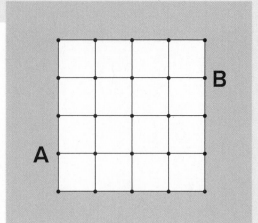

Words at Work   A coach buys some new balls, bats, and gloves for
the baseball team. She buys 10 things in total.

a. Draw a picture to show how many balls, bats, and gloves
there could be.

b. Write a sentence to describe your picture.

1. Look at the blocks. Write the matching number on the expanders.

a.

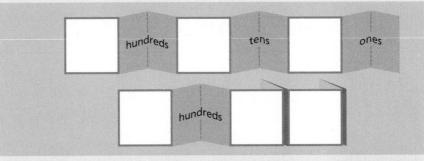

hundreds   tens   ones

hundreds

b.

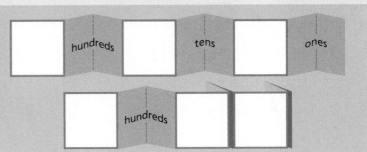

hundreds   tens   ones

hundreds

2. Draw ⌢ to show two numbers that make 10.
Write an equation to show how you add to find the total.

a.

3   3   7

[ ] + [ ] + [ ] = [ ]

b.

4   5   5

[ ] + [ ] + [ ] = [ ]

Write the missing numbers on these number track pieces.

a.

| | 8 | |

b.

| | 10 | |

FROM 1.7.2

FROM 1.8.2

Step In

What two addition facts match this picture?

Which fact do you think is easier to figure out? Why?

I find it easier to figure out 9 + 4, then write the turnaround.

Step Up

1. Write an addition fact to match each picture. Then write the turnaround fact.

a.

☐ + ☐ = ☐

☐ + ☐ = ☐

b.

☐ + ☐ = ☐

☐ + ☐ = ☐

c.

☐ + ☐ = ☐

☐ + ☐ = ☐

d.

☐ + ☐ = ☐

☐ + ☐ = ☐

e.

☐ + ☐ = ☐

☐ + ☐ = ☐

f.

☐ + ☐ = ☐

☐ + ☐ = ☐

2. Write an addition fact to match each picture.
Then write the turnaround fact.

a.

☐ + ☐ = ☐

☐ + ☐ = ☐

b.

☐ + ☐ = ☐

☐ + ☐ = ☐

c.

☐ + ☐ = ☐

☐ + ☐ = ☐

d.

☐ + ☐ = ☐

☐ + ☐ = ☐

e.

☐ + ☐ = ☐

☐ + ☐ = ☐

f.

☐ + ☐ = ☐

☐ + ☐ = ☐

Step Ahead

a. Add the numbers in each row. Then add the numbers in each column. Write the totals around the outside.

8	1	6	☐
3	5	7	☐
4	9	2	☐
☐	☐	☐	

b. Write an equation to show three other numbers that will add to make the same total.

☐ + ☐ + ☐ = ☐

Step In

Look at these pictures.
How could each picture show addition?

How could you figure out the total in each picture?
Which addition strategy would you use?

Which addition strategy would you use to solve each of these facts?

6 + 7 = ☐

2 + 9 = ☐

5 + 8 = ☐

How can different strategies be used to solve the same fact?

Step Up

I. Write the total. Then write
C, D, or **M** in the circle to
show the strategy you used
to figure out the total.

Addition strategy

Ⓒ count-on

Ⓓ doubles

Ⓜ make-ten

○ 8 + 0 = ☐

○ 9 + 5 = ☐

○ 5 + 6 = ☐

○ 3 + 9 = ☐

○ 2 + 5 = ☐

○ 8 + 8 = ☐

○ 9 + 2 = ☐

○ 7 + 9 = ☐

2. Write the answer. Then draw a line to the strategy you used to figure it out.

$2 + 6 = \boxed{}$

$9 + 3 = \boxed{}$

$7 + 8 = \boxed{}$

$9 + 9 = \boxed{}$

$9 + 6 = \boxed{}$

count-on

doubles

make-ten

$3 + 1 = \boxed{}$

$7 + 5 = \boxed{}$

$1 + 7 = \boxed{}$

$6 + 8 = \boxed{}$

$5 + 9 = \boxed{}$

Step Ahead

You can use more than one strategy to solve the same fact. Complete these to show the different ways these totals can be figured out.

a. Use the make-ten strategy

$9 + 8 = \underline{}$

is the same value as

$10 + \underline{} = \underline{}$

Use the doubles strategy

$9 + 8 = \underline{}$

is the same value as

double 8 plus $\underline{} = \underline{} \; \underline{}$

b. Use the make-ten strategy

$8 + 6 = \underline{}$

is the same value as

$10 + \underline{} = \underline{}$

Use the doubles strategy

$8 + 6 = \underline{}$

is the same value as

double 6 plus $\underline{} = \underline{} \; \underline{}$

Computation Practice

★ Complete the equations.
★ Use the same color to show keys and locks with matching answers. One key does not have a match.

15 – 7 =

5 – 2 =

9 – 4 =

7 – 4 =

13 – 6 =

15 – 8 =

9 – 5 =

13 – 7 =

11 – 5 =

7 – 3 =

17 – 9 =

17 – 8 =

11 – 6 =

1. Figure out the number of dots that are covered. Then complete the facts.

a. 16 − 7 = ☐

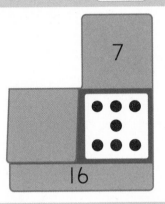

7 + ☐ = 16

b. 12 − 5 = ☐

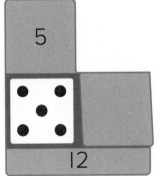

5 + ☐ = 12

c. 14 − 6 = ☐

6 + ☐ = 14

2. Draw more counters. Then write the numbers to match.

a. Draw 6 more.

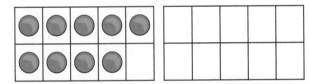

see ☐ + ☐

think ☐ + ☐

b. Draw 4 more.

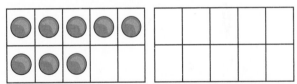

see ☐ + ☐

think ☐ + ☐

Preparing for Module 9

Draw jumps to help you count on. Write two addition facts to match.

Count on **2**.

| 11 | 12 | 13 | 14 | 15 | 16 | 17 | 18 | 19 | 20 |

☐ + ☐ = ☐

☐ + ☐ = ☐

FROM 1.7.8

FROM 1.8.3

Step In

What is wrong with this balance picture?

How many more circles do you need to draw to make the balance picture true?

Draw the circles on the picture.

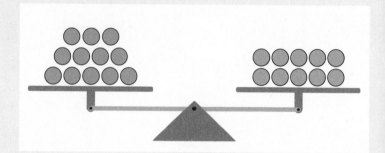

What equation could you write to match the picture?

☐ = ☐ + ☐

Step Up

1. Draw **more circles** on one side of each pan balance to make the balance picture true. Then write the matching equation.

a.

6 + ☐ = 8

b.

☐ = ☐ + ☐

c.

☐ = ☐ + ☐

d.

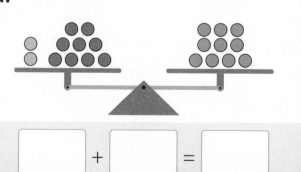

☐ + ☐ = ☐

2. Write the missing numeral to make each balance picture true. Then write the matching equation.

a.

| 13 | 2 | | ☐ |

☐ + ☐ = ☐

b.

| 15 | | ☐ | 12 |

☐ = ☐ + ☐

c.

| 14 | | 1 | ☐ |

☐ = ☐ + ☐

d.

| 2 | 16 | | ☐ |

☐ + ☐ = ☐

e.

| ☐ | 17 | | 19 |

☐ + ☐ = ☐

f.

| 11 | | ☐ | 8 |

☐ = ☐ + ☐

Step Ahead

Write three different equations that would make this balance picture true.

☐ + ☐ = ☐

☐ + ☐ = ☐

☐ + ☐ = ☐

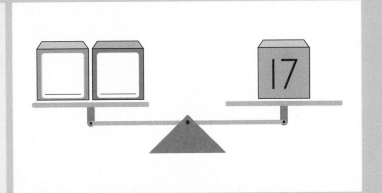

Step In Look at the circles in this balance picture.

How many more circles do you need to draw to make the balance picture true?

How do you know?

Draw the circles on the picture.

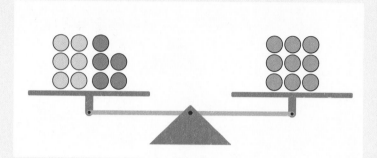

What equation could you write to match the picture?

☐ + ☐ = ☐ + ☐

Step Up I. Draw **more circles** to make each balance picture true. Then write the matching equation.

a.

$6 + 3 = 8 + \boxed{}$

b.

☐ + ☐ = ☐ + ☐

c.

☐ + ☐ = ☐ + ☐

d.

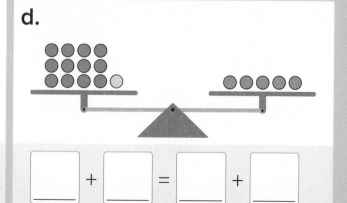

☐ + ☐ = ☐ + ☐

2. Write numerals to make each balance picture true.
Then write the matching equation.

a.

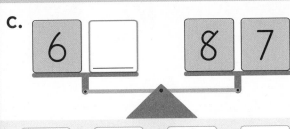

$$\boxed{5} + \boxed{6} = \boxed{7} + \boxed{}$$

b.

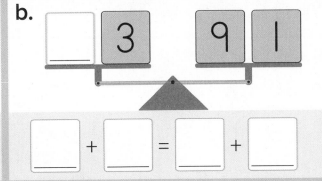

$$\boxed{} + \boxed{} = \boxed{} + \boxed{}$$

c.

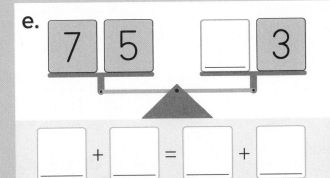

$$\boxed{} + \boxed{} = \boxed{} + \boxed{}$$

d.

$$\boxed{} + \boxed{} = \boxed{} + \boxed{}$$

e.

$$\boxed{} + \boxed{} = \boxed{} + \boxed{}$$

f.

$$\boxed{} + \boxed{} = \boxed{} + \boxed{}$$

Step Ahead Use these numbers to make each balance picture true. Each number can be used only once.

(5) (9) (4) (2)

a.

b.

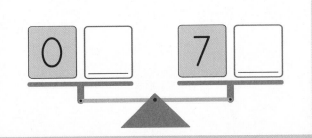

Think and Solve THINK TANK   Read the clues. Use the letters to answer.

Clues

A is heavier than **C**.

C is heavier than **B**.

A is lighter than **D**.

A   B   C   D

a.
Which is heaviest? ▢

b.
Which is lightest? ▢

Words at Work   Choose and write words from the list to complete the sentences below. One word is used more than once. Some words are not used.

| same |
| add |
| between |
| balances |
| does not |
| take away |

a.
Nine add six _____ 15.

b.
Eight add five equals ten _____ three.

c.
Eleven take two _____ four add five.

d.
Twelve take four _____ balance ten.

e. In an equation, the total value on each side of the = must

be the _____ .

Ongoing Practice

1. Complete the equations. Then write **A** on the equations that you solved by thinking about addition.

FROM 1.7.9

a. 9 – 8 = ☐

b. 10 – 4 = ☐

c. 7 – 2 = ☐

d. 4 – 4 = ☐

e. 5 – 1 = ☐

f. 6 – 5 = ☐

g. 9 – 6 = ☐

h. 11 – 8 = ☐

2. Write the missing numeral to make each balance picture true. Then write the matching equation.

FROM 1.8.7

a.

☐ + ☐ = ☐

b.

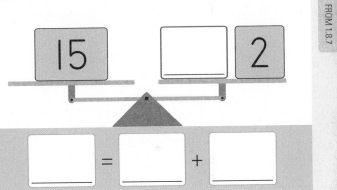

☐ = ☐ + ☐

Preparing for Module 9

Look at each picture of blocks. Write the matching number in the place-value chart. Then write the numeral without the chart.

a.

Hundreds	Tens	Ones
☐	☐	☐

☐

b.

Hundreds	Tens	Ones
☐	☐	☐

☐

Step In   Look at this balance picture.

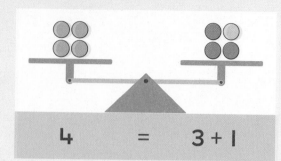

How does the picture match the equation?

| 4 | = | 3 + 1 |

Draw ○ on this pan balance to match the equation.

| 2 + 3 | = | 5 |

What does = mean?

The value on either side of the = symbol is the same.
4 is equal to 3 add 1.
2 add 3 is equal to 5.

Write the missing numeral to balance each equation.

4 + 2 = ☐   9 = 4 + ☐   ☐ + 3 = 6

Step Up   I.   Write the numeral that is missing.

a. 2 + 5 = ☐

b. 6 + 1 = ☐

c. 11 − 3 = ☐

d. ☐ = 4 + 4

e. ☐ = 5 − 0

f. ☐ = 8 + 7

2. Write **true** or **false** beside each equation.

a. $4 + 2 = 3 + 3$ _____

b. $9 = 5 + 4$ _____

c. $12 - 3 = 8$ _____

d. $7 = 9 - 2$ _____

3. Complete each equation.

a. $7 + \boxed{} = 9$

b. $\boxed{} + 4 = 12$

c. $15 - 8 = \boxed{}$

d. $5 = \boxed{} - 5$

e. $11 = \boxed{} + 9$

f. $7 = 0 + \boxed{}$

4. Write the missing number to make each equation true.

a. $3 + \boxed{} = 4 + 1$

b. $6 + 3 = 5 + \boxed{}$

c. $\boxed{} - 2 = 1 + 8$

d. $2 + \boxed{} = 5 + 6$

e. $\boxed{} + 1 = 0 + 7$

f. $3 + 5 = 14 - \boxed{}$

Step Ahead — Use these numbers to balance each equation. Each number can be used only once.

a. $3 + \boxed{} = 7 + \boxed{}$

b. $\boxed{} + 11 = 8 + \boxed{}$

$\boxed{0} \quad \boxed{1}$

$\boxed{3} \quad \boxed{5}$

Step In   These buttons are sorted into groups.

How have the buttons been sorted?

What do the marks below each group tell you?

Draw tally marks to show the number of spotted buttons.

Tally marks can be organized into groups of five.

How many buttons are there in total?

How many more buttons are plain than spotted?
Write an equation you could use to figure it out.

☐ – ☐ = ☐

Step Up   1.   Sort these buttons by **shape**. Draw tally marks
in the chart at the top of page 309 to show the
number of buttons in each group.

Shape	Tally	Total

2. Write the total number of tally marks beside each group.

3. Use the results in the table to answer each question.

a. What button shape is the most common?

b. How many buttons are shaped like a **square** or **triangle**?

c. How many buttons are shaped like a **triangle** or **circle**?

d. How many **more** buttons are shaped like a **circle** than a **square**?

e. What is the total number of buttons?

Step Ahead   Complete the missing information in this table.

Shape	Tally	Total
		12

Computation Practice

★ Complete the equations.

★ Find each total in the puzzle and color that part brown.

★ Color all the other numbered parts green.
Two parts have no numbers. Leave them white.

4 + 5 = ▢ = 5 + 4	8 + 7 = ▢ = 7 + 8	2 + 4 = ▢ = 4 + 2
3 + 1 = ▢ = 1 + 3	6 + 7 = ▢ = 7 + 6	5 + 3 = ▢ = 3 + 5
8 + 6 = ▢ = 6 + 8	7 + 5 = ▢ = 5 + 7	7 + 9 = ▢ = 9 + 7
9 + 8 = ▢ = 8 + 9	6 + 4 = ▢ = 4 + 6	3 + 4 = ▢ = 4 + 3

1. Write each time in words.

a.

b.

c.

FROM 1.7.10

_____

_____

_____

2. Write the missing numeral to make each balance picture true. Then write the matching equation.

FROM 1.8.8

a.

| 6 | 3 | | 2 | |

☐ + ☐ = ☐ + ☐

b.

| | 9 | | 3 | 7 |

☐ + ☐ = ☐ + ☐

Preparing for Module 9

Draw more counters to figure out the total. Then write the tens fact to match.

a. 9 + 5 = ☐

☐ + ☐ = ☐

b. 8 + 5 = ☐

☐ + ☐ = ☐

c. 9 + 7 = ☐

☐ + ☐ = ☐

Step In　What does this table show?

Where We Go for Lunch Recess

Place	Tally	Total
Gym	𝍷𝍷𝍷𝍷𝍷 𝍷𝍷𝍷𝍷𝍷 𝍷𝍷𝍷𝍷𝍷 ‖	
Playground	𝍷𝍷𝍷𝍷𝍷 𝍷𝍷𝍷𝍷𝍷	
Library	𝍷𝍷𝍷𝍷𝍷 ‖	

What do the marks in the **Tally** column mean?

How could you figure out what numbers to write in the **Total** column?

> I added groups of five and some ones.
> The total for the gym is 5 + 5 + 5 and 2 more.

Where is the most popular place to go for lunch recess?
Where is the least popular place to go?

How many more students go to the playground than the library?
How do you know?

> I compared the groups of tallies.
> The playground has 3 more tallies,
> so there were 3 more students there.

How many students go inside for their lunch recess?

How many students were asked where they go for lunch recess?

How did you figure out this total?

a. Write three places where your friends like to go for lunch recess.

b. Write the place names you wrote above on this chart.

Place	Tally	Total

c. Ask other students which of these places they like to go to for lunch recess. Draw tallies on the chart to show their answers.

d. Write the totals in the chart.

e. What was the most popular place? _____

f. How many students voted in total? _____

g. How many more students voted for the most popular place than the least popular place? _____

Step Ahead

Look at this tally chart.
Find and correct the two mistakes that were made.

Where We Go for Lunch Recess

Place	Tally	Total
Gym	ⅢⅢ ⅢⅢ ⅢⅢ ⅢⅢ III	23
Playground	ⅢⅢ ⅢⅢ III	13
Library	ⅢⅢ	6

Step In Three students recorded the number of vehicles in the parking lot at a weekend baseball game.

Vehicles in the Parking Lot

Vehicle	Tally	Total
Car	卌 卌 卌 卌 ||	22
Truck	卌 卌	10
Motorcycle	卌	5

Ricardo said, "There were more trucks than cars in the parking lot."

Jessica said, "There were more cars in the parking lot than trucks and motorcycles together."

Caleb said, "There were more than 30 vehicles in the parking lot."

Look at the tally chart and decide which statements are true.

What other information does the data in the tally chart tell you?

Step Up 1. Look at this tally chart. Color the ○ beside the statements that are true.

Vehicles in the Parking Lot

Vehicle	Tally	Total
Truck	卌 |||	8
Car	卌	5
Motorcycle	||	2

○ More than 10 vehicles were in the parking lot.
○ There were more motorcycles than trucks in the parking lot.
○ There were more cars than motorcycles in the parking lot.

2. Read each clue. Then write **Car**, **Truck**, and **Motorcycle** to complete each tally chart.

315 ◆

Clue 1	Clue 2
Fewer than 10 trucks were in the parking lot.	More cars than motorcycles were in the parking lot.

a.

Vehicles in the Parking Lot

Vehicle	Tally	Total
	𝍷𝍷𝍷 𝍷𝍷𝍷 𝍷𝍷𝍷 𝍷	16
	𝍷𝍷𝍷 𝍷𝍷𝍷 𝍷𝍷𝍷 𝍷𝍷𝍷 𝍷𝍷𝍷 𝍷𝍷𝍷𝍷	29
	𝍷𝍷𝍷 𝍷	6

Clue 1	Clue 2
There were 25 cars in the parking lot.	Fewer trucks than motorcycles were in the parking lot.

b.

Vehicles in the Parking Lot

Vehicle	Tally	Total
	𝍷𝍷𝍷 𝍷	6
	𝍷𝍷𝍷 𝍷𝍷𝍷 𝍷𝍷𝍷 𝍷𝍷𝍷 𝍷𝍷𝍷	25
	𝍷𝍷𝍷 𝍷𝍷𝍷 𝍷𝍷𝍷	13

Step Ahead Draw tally marks to show that 10 more trucks were in the parking lot than motorcycles.

Vehicle	Tally	Total
Truck		
Motorcycle	𝍷𝍷𝍷 𝍷𝍷	7

Think and Solve   **a.** Color pairs of numbers that **add to 10**.

5	6	2	8	0	4	5	7	10

b. Circle the leftover number.

c. Use the number you circled to complete this equation.

☐ + ☐ = 10

d. Write a pair of numbers that are **not** shown above to complete this equation.

☐ + ☐ = 10

Words at Work   Look at this tally chart. Write two sentences about the data it shows. You can use words from the list to help you.

most popular
least popular
more
fewer
how many
votes

Flowers We Like		
Flower	Tally	Total
Daisy	𝍷𝍷𝍷𝍷𝍷 |||	8
Rose	𝍷𝍷𝍷𝍷𝍷	5
Lily	𝍷𝍷𝍷𝍷𝍷 𝍷𝍷𝍷𝍷𝍷	10

_____

_____

_____

_____

_____

Ongoing Practice

1. Write these times on the digital clocks.

a.

```
┌─────────────┐
│    ⠒        │
│    ⠒        │
└─────────────┘
```

b.

```
┌─────────────┐
│    ⠒        │
│    ⠒        │
└─────────────┘
```

c.

```
┌─────────────┐
│    ⠒        │
│    ⠒        │
└─────────────┘
```

FROM 1.7.12

2. Use the tally chart to answer the questions.

FROM 1.8.10

Our Favorite Fruit

Orange	ΙΗΗΙ ΙΗΗΙ ΙΗΗΙ ΙΗΗΙ Ι
Banana	ΙΗΗΙ ΙΗΗΙ ΙΗΗΙ ΙΙΙ
Apple	ΙΗΗΙ ΙΗΗΙ ΙΙΙΙ

a. Which fruit is the most popular? _____

b. Which fruit is the least popular? _____

Preparing for Module 9   Write an addition fact to match each picture.

a.

☐ + ☐ = ☐

b.

☐ + ☐ = ☐

c.

☐ + ☐ = ☐

What two pairs of numbers keep the balance level? Use numbers from 0 to 9 only. You cannot use the same number more than once.

Show how you know.

Lifen says it is quicker to add 8 to 2 to make 10, then add the 3.

Henry says it is quicker to add the numbers in the order they appear.

Who do you agree with? Show your thinking.

 Ask for feedback. Share how the feedback helps you.

Step In Look at this part of a number track.

| 50 | 51 | 52 | 53 | 54 | 55 | 56 | 57 | 58 | 59 | 60 | 61 | 62 |

Imagine you were standing on 53 and made one jump to 55.
How can you show your jump on the number track?

You could draw an arrow like this.

| 50 | 51 | 52 | 53 | 54 | 55 | 56 | 57 | 58 | 59 | 60 | 61 | 62 |

What equation could you write to show what you did?

☐ + ☐ = ☐

What other jumps could you make on this number track?
What equations could you write to show what you did?

Step Up I. Write the totals.

| 23 | 24 | 25 | 26 | 27 | 28 | 29 | 30 | 31 | 32 | 33 |

a. 24 + 1 = ☐

b. 27 + 1 = ☐

c. 31 + 1 = ☐

2. Write the totals. Draw jumps on the number track to help you.

| 47 | 48 | 49 | 50 | 51 | 52 | 53 | 54 | 55 | 56 | 57 |

a. 49 + 1 = ☐

b. 51 + 2 = ☐

c. 54 + 3 = ☐

| 65 | 66 | 67 | 68 | 69 | 70 | 71 | 72 | 73 | 74 | 75 |

d. 66 + 1 = ☐

e. 69 + 2 = ☐

f. 72 + 3 = ☐

3. Use this number track to complete different equations.

| 84 | 85 | 86 | 87 | 88 | 89 | 90 | 91 | 92 | 93 | 94 |

a. ☐ + 2 = ☐

b. ☐ + 1 = ☐

c. ☐ + 3 = ☐

d. ☐ + 2 = ☐

e. ☐ + 1 = ☐

f. ☐ + 3 = ☐

Step Ahead Use the number track in Question 3 to help you figure out the answer.

Valentina has 87 cents.
Noah has 2 cents more than Valentina.
Mary has 3 cents more than Noah.
Ryan has 2 cents more than Mary.

How much money does Ryan have?

☐ cents

Step In

Two friends play a game.
They take turns to roll the cubes.
They then move their counter to
match what they roll.

1	2	3	4	5	6	7	8	9	10
11	12	13	14	15	16	17	18	19	20
21	22	23	24	25	26	27	28	29	(30)
31	32	33	(34)	35	36	37	38	39	40
41	42	43	44	45	46	47	48	49	50

Adianna has the yellow
counter. She rolls **10 less**.

What number should she
move her counter to?

Max has the purple counter.
He rolls **1 greater**.

What number should he
move his counter to?

Janice joins the game.
She starts on 17, rolls **10 greater**, and then rolls **1 less**.
What number does she finish on?

Step Up

1. These are parts of a hundred chart.
   Write the missing numbers.

a. ☐ | 37 | ☐

b. ☐ / 75 | ☐

c. ☐ / 49 / ☐

d. ☐ / 22 / ☐

2. Write numbers that are **1 greater** and **1 less**.

	45			13			68	

	50			25			97	

3. Write numbers that are **10 greater** and **10 less**.

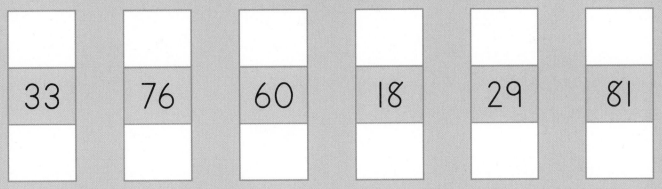

4. Solve each problem.

a. 2 friends are reading the same book. Layla has read 10 more pages than Cody. Cody has read 42 pages. How many pages has Layla read?

_____ pages

b. Victor has sold 83 tickets for a charity. He has sold one more ticket than Nancy. How many tickets has Nancy sold?

_____ tickets

Step Ahead Look at this part of a hundred chart. Use the list to write the missing numbers. Cross out the numbers not shown.

45	55	36	37
34	38	65	33

Computation Practice   **What has four legs but does not walk?**

★ Complete the equations.

★ Use a ruler to draw a straight line to join matching totals. Each line will pass through a letter.

★ Write the letter above its matching total at the bottom of the page.

$3 + 9 =$ ☐ ▶

◀ ☐ $= 9 + 6$

$8 + 7 =$ ☐ ▶

◀ ☐ $= 8 + 3$

$5 + 8 =$ ☐ ▶

◀ ☐ $= 9 + 5$

$9 + 2 =$ ☐ ▶

◀ ☐ $= 5 + 7$

$8 + 6 =$ ☐ ▶

◀ ☐ $= 4 + 9$

$7 + 9 =$ ☐ ▶

◀ ☐ $= 8 + 8$

l   t   a   b   a   e

☐ ☐ ☐ ☐ ☐ ☐

11   12   13   14   15   16

Ongoing Practice

1. Draw **more** counters to figure out the total.
Fill the ten-frame first. Then write the tens fact
to match the picture.

a.
9 + 4 = ☐

☐ + ☐ = ☐

b.
9 + 7 = ☐

☐ + ☐ = ☐

c.
8 + 5 = ☐

☐ + ☐ = ☐

2. Write the totals. Draw jumps on the number track to help you.

| 37 | 38 | 39 | 40 | 41 | 42 | 43 | 44 | 45 | 46 | 47 |

a.
38 + 1 = ☐

b.
40 + 2 = ☐

c.
42 + 3 = ☐

Preparing for Module 10

Write the answers. You can draw jumps
on the number track to help you.

| 1 | 2 | 3 | 4 | 5 | 6 | 7 | 8 | 9 | 10 |

a.
7 − 2 = ☐

b.
10 − 2 = ☐

c.
8 − 1 = ☐

Step In   Look at these numbers.

1	2	3	4	5	6	7	8	9	10
11	12	13	14	15	16	17	18	19	20
21	22	23	24	25	26	27	28	29	30
31	32	33	34	35	36	37	38	39	40
41	42	43	44	45	46	47	48	49	50

What number is **1 more** than 37?
How do you know?

What number is **2 more** than 25?
How do you know?

What do you know about all the numbers that have 9 in the ones place?

Step Up   1.   Write the totals.

a.
2 + 1 = ☐

12 + 1 = ☐

22 + 1 = ☐

32 + 1 = ☐

52 + 1 = ☐

72 + 1 = ☐

b.
14 + 2 = ☐

24 + 2 = ☐

34 + 2 = ☐

44 + 2 = ☐

64 + 2 = ☐

84 + 2 = ☐

c.
5 + 3 = ☐

15 + 3 = ☐

25 + 3 = ☐

35 + 3 = ☐

75 + 3 = ☐

95 + 3 = ☐

2. Write numbers **between 1 and 50** to match.

a. All the numbers that have 3 in the ones place.

b. The numbers that are **2 more** than each number above.

3. Write numbers **between 50 and 100** to match.

a. All the numbers that have 6 in the ones place.

b. The numbers that are **2 more** than each number above.

4. Write numbers **between 11 and 50** to complete these to show different equations.

a.

$\boxed{} + 3 = \boxed{}$

b.

$\boxed{} + 2 = \boxed{}$

c.

$\boxed{} + 1 = \boxed{}$

Step Ahead

John has 55 cents. He finds 4 cents more. Teresa has 56 cents. Her mom gives her 2 cents more. Riku has 58 cents.

a. Who has the most money in total? $\boxed{}$

b. Write the equations you used to help you.

Addition: Any two-digit number and 1, 2, 3 or 10, 20, 30 (hundred chart)

Step In

Look at this part of a hundred chart.

1	2	3	4	5	6	7	8	9	10
11	12	13	14	15	16	17	18	19	20

What happens to the numbers as you move from left to right?

What happens to the numbers as you move down the rows?

Look at this part of the same hundred chart.
What numbers are missing? How do you know?

Look at this part of the hundred chart.
What numbers could you write in the white spaces?
How do you know?

Step Up   1.   Write the totals. You can use the chart to help.

a.
63 + 1 =

b.
47 + 10 =

c.
78 + 2 =

41	42	43	44	45	46	47	48	49	50
51	52	53	54	55	56	57	58	59	60
61	62	63	64	65	66	67	68	69	70
71	72	73	74	75	76	77	78	79	80
81	82	83	84	85	86	87	88	89	90

d.
52 + 20 =

e.
74 + 10 =

f.
59 + 20 =

2. Figure out and write the totals.

a. $88 + 10 =$ ▢

b. $27 + 2 =$ ▢

c. $31 + 20 =$ ▢

d. $16 + 10 =$ ▢

e. $36 + 2 =$ ▢

f. $73 + 20 =$ ▢

g. $93 + 2 =$ ▢

h. $42 + 30 =$ ▢

i. $26 + 20 =$ ▢

j. $49 + 0 =$ ▢

k. $10 + 56 =$ ▢

l. $30 + 61 =$ ▢

Step Ahead Write the missing numbers along the trail.

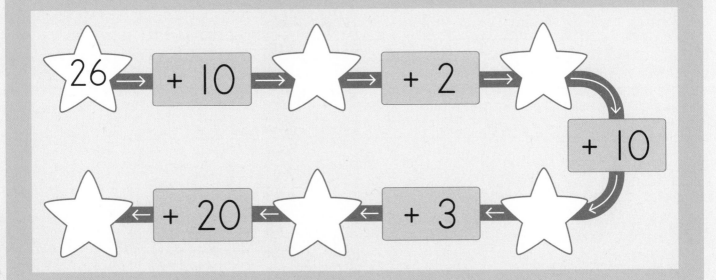

© ORIGO Education

Think and Solve Write a number to make each balance picture true.

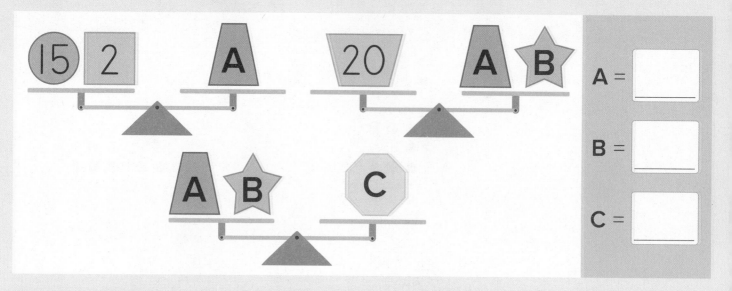

A = ____

B = ____

C = ____

Words at Work

Write about **adding on a hundred chart**. You can use words from the list to help you.

up	down	across
tens	ones	add
total	move	count on

1	2	3	4	5	6	7	8	9	10
11	12	13	14	15	16	17	18	19	20
21	22	23	24	25	26	27	28	29	30
31	32	33	34	35	36	37	38	39	40
41	42	43	44	45	46	47	48	49	50
51	52	53	54	55	56	57	58	59	60
61	62	63	64	65	66	67	68	69	70
71	72	73	74	75	76	77	78	79	80
81	82	83	84	85	86	87	88	89	90
91	92	93	94	95	96	97	98	99	100

Ongoing Practice

1. Write an addition fact to match each picture. Then write the turnaround fact.

a.

☐ + ☐ = ☐

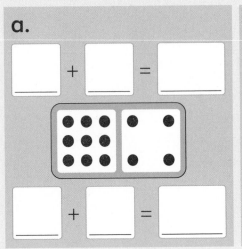

☐ + ☐ = ☐

b.

☐ + ☐ = ☐

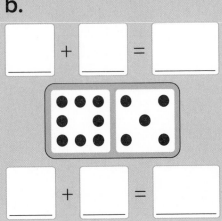

☐ + ☐ = ☐

c.

☐ + ☐ = ☐

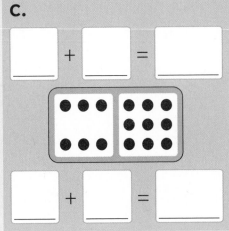

☐ + ☐ = ☐

2. These are parts of a hundred chart. Write the missing numbers.

a.

	57	

b.

35

c.

69

d.

42

Preparing for Module 10

Complete the addition fact to figure out the carrots that were taken. Then complete the subtraction fact.

a.

____ + ____ = ____

____ – ____ = ____

b.

____ + ____ = ____

____ – ____ = ____

Step In Look at this part of a hundred chart.

How can you figure out what number is behind the shaded tile?

31	32	33	34	35
				45
		52		

I would start at 34 and add groups of 10 to the shaded tile.

How many groups of 10 would you add?

What equation could you write to match?

□ + □ = □

How could you use the hundred chart to figure out 52 + 20?

Step Up I. Write the totals. You can use this part of a hundred chart to help.

1	2	3	4	5	6	7	8	9	10
11	12	13	14	15	16	17	18	19	20
21	22	23	24	25	26	27	28	29	30
31	32	33	34	35	36	37	38	39	40
41	42	43	44	45	46	47	48	49	50
51	52	53	54	55	56	57	58	59	60

a. 29 + 20 = ___

b. 16 + 30 = ___

c. 14 + 40 = ___

2. Write the totals. Use this part of a hundred chart to help.

51	52	53	54	55	56	57	58	59	60
61	62	63	64	65	66	67	68	69	70
71	72	73	74	75	76	77	78	79	80
81	82	83	84	85	86	87	88	89	90
91	92	93	94	95	96	97	98	99	100

a. $87 + 10 =$ ☐

b. $54 + 40 =$ ☐

c. $69 + 30 =$ ☐

d. $73 + 20 =$ ☐

e. $57 + 30 =$ ☐

f. $55 + 40 =$ ☐

3. Write these totals.

a. $33 + 50 =$ ☐

b. $25 + 40 =$ ☐

c. $38 + 60 =$ ☐

d. $57 + 30 =$ ☐

e. $15 + 70 =$ ☐

f. $21 + 50 =$ ☐

Step Ahead

Leila has 90 cents. She wants to buy two pieces of fruit. Write equations to show all the possible combinations she can buy.

23 cents   37 cents   40 cents   60 cents

☐ + ☐ = ☐   ☐ + ☐ = ☐

☐ + ☐ = ☐   ☐ + ☐ = ☐

Step In

Look at this part of a hundred chart.

How would you move the counter to show 12 + 10?

How would you move the counter to show 12 + 2?

How would you move the counter to show 12 + 12?

1	2	3	4	5	6
11	12	13	14	15	16
21	22	23	24	25	26
31	32	33	34	35	36
41	42	43	44	45	46

How would you use the hundred chart to figure out 23 + 21?

Step Up

1. Draw arrows on this hundred chart to show how you add. Then write the totals. The first one has been done for you.

a. 31 + 12 = 43

b. 52 + 21 = ☐

c. 27 + 32 = ☐

d. 45 + 11 = ☐

e. 64 + 23 = ☐

f. 57 + 21 = ☐

g. 83 + 13 = ☐

h. 69 + 21 = ☐

1	2	3	4	5	6	7	8	9	10
11	12	13	14	15	16	17	18	19	20
21	22	23	24	25	26	27	28	29	30
31	32	33	34	35	36	37	38	39	40
41	42	43	44	45	46	47	48	49	50
51	52	53	54	55	56	57	58	59	60
61	62	63	64	65	66	67	68	69	70
71	72	73	74	75	76	77	78	79	80
81	82	83	84	85	86	87	88	89	90
91	92	93	94	95	96	97	98	99	100

2. Write the number at the end of each part of a hundred chart.
Then complete the matching equation.

a.

37

$\boxed{37} + \boxed{22} = \boxed{}$

b.

71

$\boxed{} + \boxed{} = \boxed{}$

c.

45

$\boxed{} + \boxed{} = \boxed{}$

d.

52

$\boxed{} + \boxed{} = \boxed{}$

Step Ahead

Thomas added tens and then ones to figure out
35 + 13. Use his strategy to figure out 46 + 21.

$35 + 13 = 48$

35	45	
46	47	48

$46 + 21 = ?$

46		

Computation Practice   **What does an egg do if you tell it a joke?**

★ Complete the equations. Then write each letter above its matching answer in the box below. One letter appears more than once.

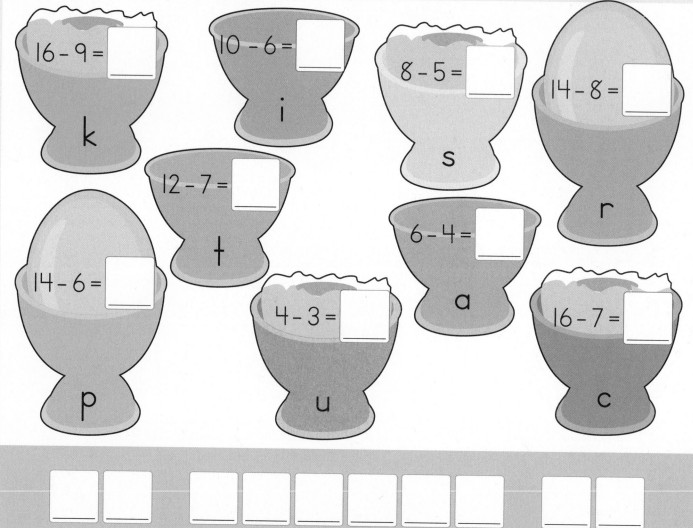

16 − 9 = ☐ k

10 − 6 = ☐ i

8 − 5 = ☐ s

14 − 8 = ☐ r

12 − 7 = ☐ t

6 − 4 = ☐ a

14 − 6 = ☐ p

4 − 3 = ☐ u

16 − 7 = ☐ c

☐	☐		☐	☐	☐	☐	☐	☐		☐	☐
4	5		9	6	2	9	7	3		1	8

Complete the equations as fast as you can.

10 − 7 = ☐   10 − 4 = ☐   8 − 3 = ☐

9 − 5 = ☐   4 − 1 = ☐   6 − 2 = ☐

1. Write an addition fact to match each picture. Then write the turnaround fact.

a.

☐ + ☐ = ☐

:·: | 9

☐ + ☐ = ☐

b.

☐ + ☐ = ☐

6 | :::

☐ + ☐ = ☐

c.

☐ + ☐ = ☐

::: | 3

☐ + ☐ = ☐

2. Write the totals. Use the chart to help.

41	42	43	44	45	46	47	48	49	50
51	52	53	54	55	56	57	58	59	60
61	62	63	64	65	66	67	68	69	70
71	72	73	74	75	76	77	78	79	80
81	82	83	84	85	86	87	88	89	90

a. $65 + 10 =$ ☐

b. $42 + 40 =$ ☐

c. $59 + 20 =$ ☐

d. $45 + 20 =$ ☐

Preparing for Module 10

Count on or count back to figure out these. Draw jumps on the number track to show your thinking.

| 1 | 2 | 3 | 4 | 5 | 6 | 7 | 8 | 9 | 10 | 11 | 12 | 13 | 14 | 15 |

a. $4 - 1 =$ ☐

b. $11 - 7 =$ ☐

c. $15 - 3 =$ ☐

Step In

How can you figure out the total cost of these two pieces of fruit?

 50 cents

 30 cents

Mia used this chart.

$50 + 30 =$

$50 + 30 = 80$

How do the blocks on the chart match the price tags?

How do you think she figured out the total cost?

How would you use this chart to figure out 42 + 5?

Draw tens and ones blocks on the right to show the total.

$42 + 5 =$

$42 + 5 = \boxed{}$

Step Up

1. Add the two groups. Then write the matching equation. Use blocks to help you.

a. 50   20

[ ] + [ ] = [ ]

b. 40   50

[ ] + [ ] = [ ]

2. Add the two groups. Then write the matching equation.
Use blocks to help you.

a. 30 | 4

☐ + ☐ = ☐

b. 51 | 7

☐ + ☐ = ☐

c. 63 | 5

☐ + ☐ = ☐

d. 6 | 21

☐ + ☐ = ☐

3. Write each total. Use blocks to help your thinking.

a. 30 + 30 = ☐

b. 10 + 60 = ☐

c. 40 + 9 = ☐

d. 3 + 50 = ☐

e. 25 + 3 = ☐

f. 72 + 6 = ☐

Step Ahead

Write equations to show four
different ways these coins could
be split between two people.

_____ + _____ = 90

_____ + _____ = 90

_____ + _____ = 90

_____ + _____ = 90

Step In Look at these scoreboards.

How can you figure out the total number of points scored by the Blue Team?

Andrew used this chart.

17 + 32 =		

➡️

17 + 32 = 49

What steps do you think he used?

How would you use the chart to figure out the total for the Red Team?

How could you figure out the total in your head?

I would start with 23 then add the tens and ones of the other number. 23 + 25 **is the same value as** 23 + 20 + 5.

I would add the tens first, then the ones. 23 + 25 **is the same value as** 20 + 20 + 3 + 5.

What other way could you add to find the total?

1. Figure out the total for each team. Use blocks to help. Then write a matching equation.

Team A		Team B		Team C	
Peta 51	Nathan 14	Oscar 45	Sheree 34	Carlos 26	Nicole 33

☐ + ☐ = ☐   ☐ + ☐ = ☐   ☐ + ☐ = ☐

2. Figure out the total for each team in your head. Write an equation to show your thinking.

Team A		Team B		Team C	
Stella 43	Dixon 24	Beatrice 31	Gabriel 32	Shiro 52	Grace 17

Team D		Team E		Team F	
Owen 23	Camila 22	Allan 26	Ashley 12	Fiona 16	Hugo 11

Look at the total points scored by these teams. Write a pair of possible scores on each board. Then write the matching equation.

Green Team 84 total points		Blue Team 67 total points		Yellow Team 76 total points	
Mateo	Charlotte	Cathy	Carey	Carmen	Ethan

☐ + ☐ = ☐   ☐ + ☐ = ☐   ☐ + ☐ = ☐

Think and Solve Look at this rectangle.

Draw one more line to make 2 equal parts.

What shape is each part?

Words at Work Write the answer for each clue in the grid.
Use words from the list.

Clues Across

1. 39 plus 23 __ 62.

4. You can show __ on a hundred chart.

6. You can draw __ on a number track to show how to add.

Clues Down

2. 47 __ 17 makes a total of 64.

3. 8 tens and 14 ones shows the same number as __ tens and 4 ones.

5. Ten ones blocks is the same value as one __ block.

add
addition
jumps
equals
nine
tens

Ongoing Practice

1. Draw tally marks in the chart to show the number of socks in each group. Then write the total number of tally marks beside each group.

Socks	Tally	Total
Plain		
Striped		
Spotted		

2. Add the two groups. Write the matching equation.

a. 60   30

☐ + ☐ = ☐

b. 20   70

☐ + ☐ = ☐

Preparing for Module 10   Count on to 10. Write the addition fact.

a.

| 0 | 1 | 2 | 3 | 4 | 5 | 6 | 7 | 8 | 9 | 10 |

$9 + \boxed{} = 10$

b.

| 0 | 1 | 2 | 3 | 4 | 5 | 6 | 7 | 8 | 9 | 10 |

$7 + \boxed{} = 10$

Step In Jennifer uses this chart to figure out **39 + 3.**

39 + 3 =

39 + 3 =

What does Jennifer need to do to figure out the total?

The 12 ones blocks can be regrouped as 1 ten and 2 ones.

Jennifer regroups the ones blocks.

39 + 3 =

39 + 3 = 42

How does she regroup the ones blocks? What is the total?

Step Up 1. Write the number of ones blocks. Circle 10 ones. Then write the number of tens and ones.

a.

_____ ones

_____ ten _____ ones

b.

_____ ones

_____ ten _____ ones

2. Add the two groups. Write the matching equation. Use blocks to help you.

a. 29   2

☐ + ☐ = ☐

b. 48   5

☐ + ☐ = ☐

c. 35   6

☐ + ☐ = ☐

d. 4   57

☐ + ☐ = ☐

3. Write each total. You can use blocks to help your thinking.

a. 19 + 3 = ☐

b. 47 + 5 = ☐

c. 27 + 4 = ☐

d. 6 + 55 = ☐

e. 3 + 37 = ☐

f. 79 + 5 = ☐

Step Ahead

Color the statements that are true. Use blocks to help your thinking.

3 tens 14 ones **shows the same number as** 4 tens and 4 ones	5 tens 12 ones **shows the same number as** 7 tens and 2 ones
4 tens 10 ones **shows the same number as** 5 tens and 0 ones	7 tens 17 ones **shows the same number as** 9 tens and 7 ones

Step In   Imagine you have 70 cents.

Do you have enough money to buy both toys?

25 cents
47 cents

How could you figure out the total cost of the two toys?

Antonio uses this chart to figure out the total.

47 + 25 =   47 + 25 =

There are 6 tens and 12 ones. I can figure out the total by adding 60 + 12, or I can regroup some of the ones blocks.

Antonio regroups the ones blocks.

47 + 25 =   47 + 25 =   72

How does Antonio regroup the ones blocks? What is the total?
What is another way to figure out the total?

1. Add the two groups. Write the matching equation. Use blocks to help you.

a. 39 12

☐ + ☐ = ☐

b. 17 45

☐ + ☐ = ☐

c. 35 28

☐ + ☐ = ☐

d. 38 47

☐ + ☐ = ☐

2. Write each total. You can use blocks to help your thinking.

a. 29 + 22 = ☐

b. 32 + 18 = ☐

c. 46 + 26 = ☐

d. 23 + 58 = ☐

e. 37 + 24 = ☐

f. 36 + 27 = ☐

Step Ahead

Each brick in this wall shows the total of the two numbers directly below. Write the missing numbers.

Computation Practice

★ Complete each equation. Color each matching pair with a different color.

★ Then draw an anchor line from each ship to the anchor with the same answer.

5 – 2 =

17 – 9 =

8 – 3 =

14 – 8 =

12 – 5 =

9 – 5 =

16 – 7 =

6 – 4 =

14 – 6 =

8 – 5 =

5 – 3 =

16 – 9 =

9 – 3 =

12 – 7 =

17 – 8 =

6 – 2 =

I. **a.** Write the total number of tally marks for each.

Favorite Sea Creature		
Creature	Tally	Total
Whale	卌 |||	
Octopus	|||	
Crab	卌 卌 ||	
Shark	卌 卌 卌		

b. Which creature was the most popular?

c. How many people voted for the Whale?

2. Draw blocks to show the total. Then write a matching equation.

☐ + ☐ = ☐

Circle the pictures of 3D objects that have all flat surfaces.

Step In

What numeral would you write to match this picture of blocks?

Some of these ones blocks can be regrouped for a tens block.

Circle 10 ones blocks.
Then complete this statement.

4 tens 14 ones

shows the same number as

____ tens ____ ones

This chart was used to figure out 39 + 34.

Describe the steps that were followed.

How would you regroup the ones blocks to write the total?

Complete this statement.

6 tens 13 ones

shows the same number as

____ tens ____ ones

Step Up

1. Complete each statement. Use blocks to help you.

a.   5 tens 12 ones

shows the same number as

____ tens ____ ones

b.   3 tens 17 ones

shows the same number as

____ tens ____ ones

© ORIGO Education

2. Add the two groups. Write the matching equation.
   Write the greater number first. Use blocks to help you.

a. 55   7

[ ] + [ ] = [ ]

b. 63   29

[ ] + [ ] = [ ]

c. 8   54

[ ] + [ ] = [ ]

d. 36   39

[ ] + [ ] = [ ]

3. Write each total. Use blocks to help you.

a. 47 + 5 = [ ]

b. 29 + 15 = [ ]

c. 7 + 34 = [ ]

d. 61 + 19 = [ ]

e. 4 + 89 = [ ]

f. 27 + 25 = [ ]

Step Ahead   Jacinta added these two groups. [ ]
                  Write the correct total.

Then talk about the mistake that was made with the student beside you.

27 + 14 =   →   27 + 14 = 311

Step In What addition story could you write about this picture?

What equation could you write to match your story?

Harvey puts some money in his pocket. He then finds another two dimes under the sofa. He now has a total of 65 cents. How much money was in his pocket before his find?

Step Up I. Draw a picture of coins to represent this story. Then write an equation to match.

Emily has 6 dimes. Each dime is 10 cents. She finds one more dime and 2 pennies. How much money does she have now?

60 +

© ORIGO Education

2. Solve each problem. Show your thinking.

a. Michelle has 40 cents. She finds more money under the bed. She now has 90 cents. How much money did she find?

_____ cents

b. Juan has 48 cents and his friend has 27 cents. Juan's aunt gives him 30 cents. How much money does Juan have now?

_____ cents

c. Ringo has saved 75 cents. His sister has saved 40 cents. How much more money has Ringo saved?

_____ cents

d. A small pencil costs 49 cents. A large pencil costs 25 cents more. What is the cost of a large pencil?

_____ cents

Step Ahead

Corey finds two quarters on the ground. Each quarter is 25 cents. He now has 90 cents in total. How much money did he have before?

_____ cents

Think and Solve Imagine this pattern keeps going.

| Shape | 1 | 2 | 3 | 4 | 5 | 6 | 7 | 8 | 9 | 18 |

a. Draw Shape 18 in the white box.

b. Circle the repeating part.

c. Imagine the pattern showed seven repeating parts.
Write the number of squares and triangles there would be.

_____ squares   _____ triangles

Words at Work   a. Write a word problem to solve using addition.
Use numbers that have some tens and ones.

b. Draw a picture to show your problem.

Ongoing Practice

1. Use the tally chart to answer the questions.

FROM 1.8.12

Our Favorite Color

Red	₸₸₸ ₸₸₸ ‖
Blue	₸₸₸ ₸₸₸ ₸₸₸ ‖
Purple	₸₸₸ ‖‖

a. Which color is the most popular? _____

b. Which color is the least popular? _____

2. Figure out the total. Write an equation to match.

FROM 1.9.10

a.

_____

b.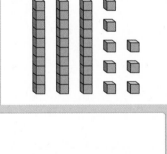

_____

Preparing for Module 10

Draw a line from each shape to its matching name.

circle

square

triangle

Anna's basketball team has scored a total of 88 points in two games. The team scored 40 or more points in each game.

How many points could have been scored in each game?

Show how you know.

73 + ___ = ___

Hernando is thinking about adding numbers to 73.

He says it is impossible to add a number greater than or equal to 27 and have a two-digit number as the sum.

Do you agree with Hernando? Show your thinking.

Ask for feedback. Share how the feedback helps you.

Step In   Look at this picture. What do you see?

$$6 - 1 = 5$$

How does each equation match the picture?
What do the numbers in each equation tell you?

$$6 - 5 = 1$$

What stays the same in each equation?
What changes?

> (i) A subtraction fact does not have a turnaround fact. It has a **related** fact.

Step Up   **I.**   Write numbers to match each picture.

a.

_____ frogs in total

_____ frogs are out

_____ frogs are in

$7 - 2 =$ _____

_____ frogs in total

_____ frogs are in

_____ frogs are out

$7 - 5 =$ _____

b.

_____ sheep in total

_____ sheep are out

_____ sheep are in

$9 - 4 =$ _____

_____ sheep in total

_____ sheep are in

_____ sheep are out

$9 - 5 =$ _____

2. Write the missing numbers.

a.

$5 - 1 = $ ⬜

$5 - 4 = $ ⬜

b.

$8 - 5 = $ ⬜

$8 - 3 = $ ⬜

c.

$12 - 9 = $ ⬜

$12 - 3 = $ ⬜

d.

$11 - 4 = $ ⬜

$11 - 7 = $ ⬜

Step Ahead

Draw a subtraction picture.
Then write two related subtraction facts to match.

⬜ − ⬜ = ⬜

⬜ − ⬜ = ⬜

Step In   What do you notice about this picture?

What is the total number of hats?
How many hats have a star?
How many hats do not have a star?

How does each of these subtraction facts
match the picture?

What does each number in the equations tell you?

$$7 - 3 = 4$$

$$7 - 4 = 3$$

Step Up   I.   Write two subtraction facts to match each picture.

a.

$$5 - 2 = 3$$

$$5 - 3 = 2$$

b.

$$\boxed{} - \boxed{} = \boxed{}$$

$$\boxed{} - \boxed{} = \boxed{}$$

2. Color some of the pictures. Then write the two subtraction facts to match.

a.

☐ − ☐ = ☐

☐ − ☐ = ☐

b.

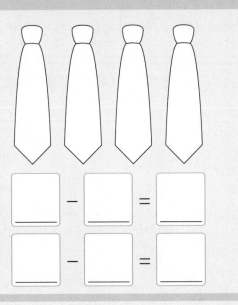

☐ − ☐ = ☐

☐ − ☐ = ☐

c.

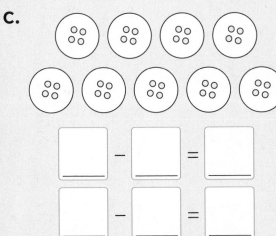

☐ − ☐ = ☐

☐ − ☐ = ☐

d.

☐ − ☐ = ☐

☐ − ☐ = ☐

Step Ahead   Write the related subtraction fact for each of these.

a.   9 − 7 = 2

9 − 2 = 7

b.   5 − 1 = 4

☐ − ☐ = ☐

c.   9 − 3 = 6

☐ − ☐ = ☐

d.   10 − 4 = 6

☐ − ☐ = ☐

e.   6 − 0 = 6

☐ − ☐ = ☐

f.   13 − 6 = 7

☐ − ☐ = ☐

Computation Practice   **Why can't elephants drive cars?**

★ Complete the equations.
★ Write each letter in the box above its matching total at the bottom of the page. Some letters are used more than once.

10 + 2 = ☐ **b**   3 + 14 = ☐ **r**   6 + 1 = ☐ **s**

2 + 11 = ☐ **o**   6 + 3 = ☐ **t**   3 + 2 = ☐ **h**

18 + 2 = ☐ **d**   1 + 10 = ☐ **f**   1 + 15 = ☐ **a**

2 + 6 = ☐ **i**   7 + 3 = ☐ **g**   17 + 1 = ☐ **l**

13 + 1 = ☐ **e**   3 + 16 = ☐ **p**

9	5	14	8	17	11	14	14	9	16	17	14

9	13	13	12	8	10	11	13	17

9	5	14	19	14	20	16	18	7

1. Write **<**, **>**, or **=** to make true comparisons.

a.
$12 + 3 \bigcirc 2 + 14$

b.
$9 + 3 \bigcirc 6 + 8$

c.
$8 + 5 \bigcirc 9 + 2$

d.
$6 + 7 \bigcirc 7 + 8$

e.
$7 + 4 \bigcirc 9 + 2$

f.
$1 + 12 \bigcirc 9 + 9$

g.
$4 + 6 \bigcirc 7 + 3$

h.
$2 + 7 \bigcirc 5 + 1$

i.
$5 + 7 \bigcirc 8 + 8$

2. Write the missing numbers.

a.
$6 - 1 = \boxed{}$

$6 - 5 = \boxed{}$

b.
$7 - 2 = \boxed{}$

$7 - 5 = \boxed{}$

Preparing for Module 11

Draw more counters to figure out the total. Fill the ten-frame first. Then write the tens fact to match the picture.

a.
$9 + 4 = \boxed{}$

$\boxed{10} + \boxed{} = \boxed{}$

b.
$9 + 7 = \boxed{}$

$\boxed{} + \boxed{} = \boxed{}$

c.
$8 + 5 = \boxed{}$

$\boxed{} + \boxed{} = \boxed{}$

Step In   How could you figure out 50 – 20?

I can use my basic subtraction facts.
5 tens take 2 tens is 3 tens.
3 tens is the same value as 30.

I count back in jumps of 10.
50 take 10 is 40... 40 take 10 is 30.

What are two subtraction equations that involve 30 and 70?

What story would match?

I could write 70 – 30 = 40 and 70 – 40 = 30.

Bella had 70 cents and gave 30 cents to Paul.
Now she has 40 cents left.

Step Up   I.   Write two subtraction equations to match
                      each picture.

a.

50 – 40 = ___

50 – 10 = ___

b.

___ – ___ = ___

___ – ___ = ___

2. Color some of the blocks. Then write two equations to match.

a.

☐ – ☐ = ☐

☐ – ☐ = ☐

b.

☐ – ☐ = ☐

☐ – ☐ = ☐

c.

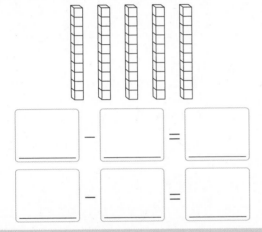

☐ – ☐ = ☐

☐ – ☐ = ☐

d.

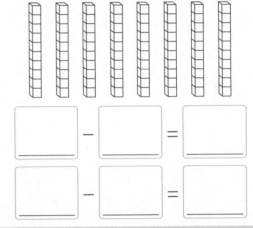

☐ – ☐ = ☐

☐ – ☐ = ☐

3. Complete each equation.
Then write a related subtraction equation.

a.

$90 - 40 =$ ☐

☐ – ☐ = ☐

b.

$80 - 70 =$ ☐

☐ – ☐ = ☐

Step Ahead   Write the missing numbers along the trail.

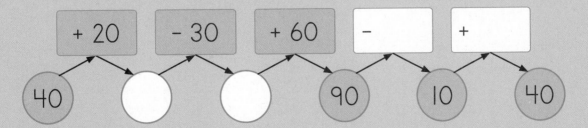

Step In   Look at this picture.

What is an addition fact that matches the picture?

What is the **turnaround** fact?

What is a subtraction fact that matches?

What is the **related** subtraction fact?

6 - 2 = 4 is related to 6 - 4 = 2.

Step Up   1. Color the animals to show two groups.
Then write an addition fact and a subtraction
fact to match each picture.

a.

b.

☐ + ☐ = ☐

☐ - ☐ = ☐

☐ + ☐ = ☐

☐ - ☐ = ☐

2. Color the animals to show two groups. Then write two addition facts and two related subtraction facts to match each picture.

a.

b.

Step Ahead

Write two addition facts and two subtraction facts to match this picture.

Think and Solve The same shapes are the same number. Write the missing number inside each triangle to complete the equation.

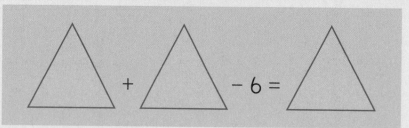

Words at Work Imagine you had some money and then you spent 10 dollars.

a. Draw a picture to show how much money you could have had at the start.

b. Write about how you figured it out.

c. Write an equation to show how much money you have left.

☐ − ☐ = ☐

1. Write the totals.

a.

27 + 1 = ☐

37 + 1 = ☐

47 + 1 = ☐

b.

16 + 2 = ☐

26 + 2 = ☐

36 + 2 = ☐

c.

4 + 3 = ☐

14 + 3 = ☐

24 + 3 = ☐

FROM 1.9.3

2. Color some of the blocks. Then write two equations to match.

a.

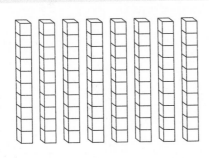

☐ – ☐ = ☐

☐ – ☐ = ☐

b.

☐ – ☐ = ☐

☐ – ☐ = ☐

FROM 1.10.3

Preparing for Module 11

Complete each fact. Then color the facts to show the thinking you used.

Strategy used

Doubles (blue)

Count on or back (red)

Make ten (green)

Think addition (yellow)

a. 6 + 1 = ☐

b. 9 + 5 = ☐

c. 7 – 3 = ☐

d. 12 – 4 = ☐

e. 8 – 2 = ☐

f. 7 + 8 = ☐

Step In   Imagine this cube train is broken into two parts.

What two addition facts could you write about the two parts?

What two subtraction facts could you write to match?

The two addition facts and the two related subtraction facts make a **fact family**.

What is another fact family you know that goes with this cube train?

Step Up   1. Write the fact family to match each picture.

a.

☐ + ☐ = ☐

☐ + ☐ = ☐

☐ − ☐ = ☐

☐ − ☐ = ☐

b.

☐ + ☐ = ☐

☐ + ☐ = ☐

☐ − ☐ = ☐

☐ − ☐ = ☐

c.

☐ + ☐ = ☐

☐ + ☐ = ☐

☐ − ☐ = ☐

☐ − ☐ = ☐

2. Draw a line from each fact to a matching picture.
Cross out the two facts that do not have a match.

6 + 3 = 9

9 − 6 = 3

2 + 5 = 7

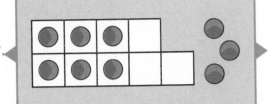

5 + 3 = 8

8 − 3 = 5

3 + 6 = 9

9 − 3 = 6

6 − 3 = 3

3 + 5 = 8

8 − 5 = 3

Step Ahead   Write the missing facts to complete each fact family.

a.

6 + 5 = 11

5 + 6 = 11

☐ − ☐ = ☐

11 − 6 = 5

b.

☐ + ☐ = ☐

6 + 7 = 13

☐ − ☐ = ☐

13 − 7 = 6

c.

☐ + ☐ = ☐

☐ + ☐ = ☐

17 − 8 = 9

☐ − ☐ = ☐

Step In   Look at this picture of cubes.

How many purple cubes are there?
How many yellow cubes are there?

How many more yellow cubes are there than purple cubes?
How could you figure it out?

How could you show your thinking on a number track?

I can count on or count back. The **difference** between the numbers is always three jumps.

Step Up   1.   Figure out the **difference** between each pair of cube trains. Then complete the equation.

a.

The difference is ☐

so 7 − 5 = ☐

b.

The difference is ☐

so 9 − 6 = ☐

c.

The difference is ☐

so 17 − 9 = ☐

2. Count the jumps to figure out the difference for each pair of shaded numbers. Then complete the equation.

a.

| 1 | 2 | 3 | 4 | 5 | 6 | 7 |

The difference is ⬚

so ⬚ − ⬚ = ⬚

b.

| 1 | 2 | 3 | 4 | 5 | 6 | 7 | 8 |

The difference is ⬚

so ⬚ − ⬚ = ⬚

3. Draw jumps to figure out the difference for each pair of shaded numbers. Then complete the equation.

a.

| 1 | 2 | 3 | 4 | 5 | 6 | 7 | 8 | 9 | 10 | 11 | 12 |

The difference is ⬚ **so** ⬚ − ⬚ = ⬚

b.

| 1 | 2 | 3 | 4 | 5 | 6 | 7 | 8 | 9 | 10 | 11 | 12 | 13 | 14 |

The difference is ⬚ **so** ⬚ − ⬚ = ⬚

c.

| 1 | 2 | 3 | 4 | 5 | 6 | 7 | 8 | 9 | 10 | 11 | 12 | 13 | 14 | 15 | 16 | 17 | 18 |

The difference is ⬚ **so** ⬚ − ⬚ = ⬚

Step Ahead Three students each find and measure a worm. Circle the two lengths that have the greatest difference.

| 13 blocks long | 11 blocks long | 4 blocks long |

Computation Practice   What does a baby elephant suck with?

★ Complete the equations.
★ Write each letter above its matching answer below.
  Some letters appear more than once.

$0 - 0 =$ ☐ i

$4 - 2 =$ ☐ c $14 - 7 =$ ☐ w $8 - 4 =$ ☐ u

$16 - 8 =$ ☐ o $18 - 9 =$ ☐ t $2 - 1 =$ ☐ h

$12 - 6 =$ ☐ m $10 - 5 =$ ☐ s $6 - 3 =$ ☐ k

☐ ☐   ☐ ☐ ☐ ☐ ☐   ☐ ☐ ☐ ☐
0 9   5 4 2 3 5   7 0 9 1

☐ ☐ ☐   ☐ ☐ ☐ ☐ ☐
0 9 5   6 8 4 9 1

Write these answers as fast as you can.

$10 - 2 =$ ☐ $8 - 3 =$ ☐ $6 - 1 =$ ☐

$2 - 0 =$ ☐ $4 - 3 =$ ☐ $7 - 2 =$ ☐

$5 - 3 =$ ☐ $9 - 3 =$ ☐ $9 - 2 =$ ☐

1. Write the answers. Use this chart to help.

a. 68 + 30 = [ ]

b. 75 + 20 = [ ]

61	62	63	64	65	66	67	68	69	70
71	72	73	74	75	76	77	78	79	80
81	82	83	84	85	86	87	88	89	90
91	92	93	94	95	96	97	98	99	100

c. 83 + 10 = [ ]

d. 79 + 20 = [ ]

e. 61 + 20 = [ ]

f. 89 + 10 = [ ]

FROM 1.9.5

2. Write the fact family to match each picture.

a.
[ ] + [ ] = [ ]
[ ] + [ ] = [ ]

[ ] − [ ] = [ ]
[ ] − [ ] = [ ]

FROM 1.10.4

b.
[ ] + [ ] = [ ]
[ ] + [ ] = [ ]

[ ] − [ ] = [ ]
[ ] − [ ] = [ ]

Preparing for Module 11

Draw a line from each coin name to its matching value.

penny

dime

nickel

10 cents

5 cents

1 cent

Step In This chipmunk has **9** acorns.

Imagine it eats 2 acorns.

How many acorns will it have left?

How can you use this number track
to figure out the answer?

| 1 | 2 | 3 | 4 | 5 | 6 | 7 | 8 | 9 | 10 |

I would start at 9 and jump **back** 2.
9 take 2 is 7, so there would be 7 acorns left.

$$-2$$
| 1 | 2 | 3 | 4 | 5 | 6 | 7 | 8 | 9 | 10 |

Imagine the chipmunk has 9 acorns and eats 6 of them.

How could you use a number track to figure out the number
of acorns it has left?

I would start at 6 and jump **on** to 9.
6 add 3 is 9, so there would be 3 acorns left.

$$+3$$
| 1 | 2 | 3 | 4 | 5 | 6 | 7 | 8 | 9 | 10 |

Write an equation to show how many acorns will be left. Use a number track on page 376 to help.

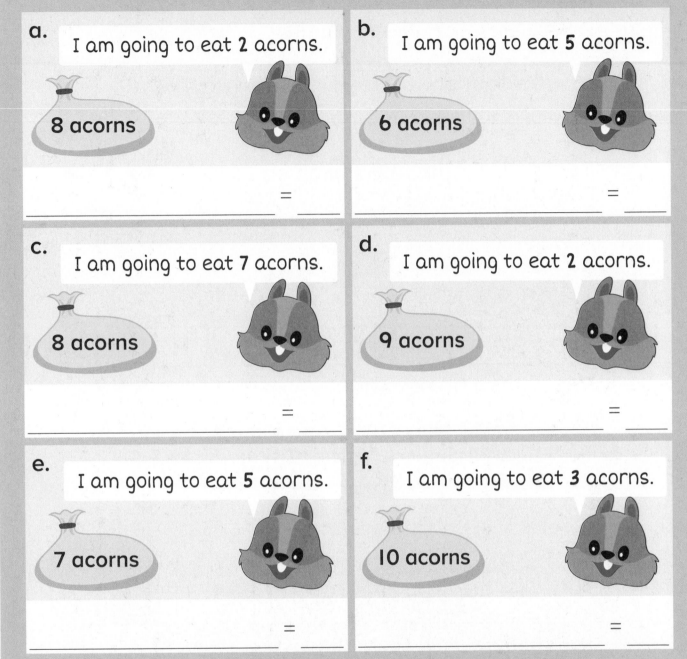

a.

I am going to eat **2** acorns.

8 acorns

_____ = _____

b.

I am going to eat **5** acorns.

6 acorns

_____ = _____

c.

I am going to eat **7** acorns.

8 acorns

_____ = _____

d.

I am going to eat **2** acorns.

9 acorns

_____ = _____

e.

I am going to eat **5** acorns.

7 acorns

_____ = _____

f.

I am going to eat **3** acorns.

10 acorns

_____ = _____

Step Ahead Solve the problem. You can draw a picture to help.

At the zoo, we buy 10 bags of animal food. In the morning, we feed 2 bags of food to the giraffes, and 5 bags to the monkeys. How many bags do we have left?

☐_____ bags

Step In   Imagine you have 7 pennies.

12 cents

How much more money do you need to buy this toy?

How could you use a number track to figure it out?

> I would start at 7 and jump on to 10.
> Then I would jump on from 10 to 12.
> 3 add 2 is 5, so I would need 5 cents.

> I would start at 12 and jump back to 10.
> Then I would jump back from 10 to 7.
> 2 add 3 is 5, so I would need 5 cents.

Step Up   1. Write how far each number is from 10.
You can use the number track to help you.

12	6	14	8	3	15

2. Figure out how much **more** money is needed to pay the price. Draw jumps on the number track to show your thinking.

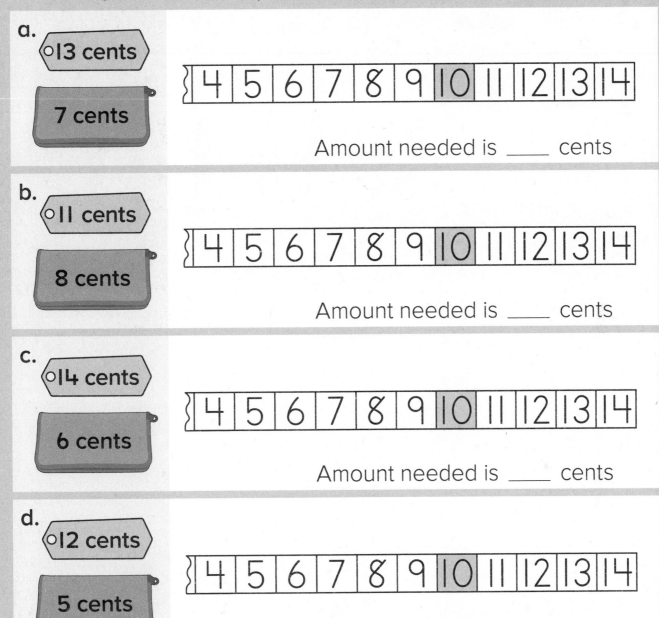

a.
○13 cents

7 cents

4 5 6 7 8 9 10 11 12 13 14

Amount needed is _____ cents

b.
○11 cents

8 cents

4 5 6 7 8 9 10 11 12 13 14

Amount needed is _____ cents

c.
○14 cents

6 cents

4 5 6 7 8 9 10 11 12 13 14

Amount needed is _____ cents

d.
○12 cents

5 cents

4 5 6 7 8 9 10 11 12 13 14

Amount needed is _____ cents

Step Ahead Write an addition or subtraction fact to match each question above.

a. _____ = ___

b. _____ = ___

c. _____ = ___

d. _____ = ___

Think and Solve Read the clues. Use the letters to answer.

Clues

X is heavier than **Y**.
Y is heavier than **Z**.
W is lighter than **Z**.

a.

Which is heaviest? _____

b.

Which is lightest? _____

Words at Work

a. Write about the parts and total in the fact family that uses these numbers.

| 7 | 12 | 5 |

_____

_____

_____

_____

b. Write equations to show your **fact family**.

1. Look at each shape. Write **true** or **false** for each fact.

Shape A		
	• It has no corners.	_____
	• It is a triangle.	_____
	• It is a closed shape.	_____

Shape B		
	• It has 5 corners.	_____
	• It is a rectangle.	_____
	• It has 4 straight sides.	_____

2. Write an equation to show how may acorns will be left.

a.

I am going to eat **4** acorns.

8 acorns

_____ = _____

b.

I am going to eat **2** acorns.

6 acorns

_____ = _____

Circle the repeating part in each pattern.

a.

b.

© ORIGO Education

FROM 1.4.10

FROM 1.10.7

Step In   **Manuel compares the number of blocks in each box.**

How many more blocks does the bigger box hold?
What equation could you write to figure out
the difference?

Hannah buys the bigger box of blocks.
She takes out 5 blocks.

How many blocks are left in the box? What equation could you write?

Step Up   I.   Solve each problem. Draw pictures or write
equations to show your thinking.

a. There are 16 blocks in a box. 3 blocks are taken out. How many blocks are left in the box?	**b.** Mika has 3 blocks. Megan has 10 blocks. How many fewer blocks does Mika have than Megan?
____ blocks	____ blocks

2. Solve each problem. Show your thinking.

a. A box holds 15 blocks. Jie uses some blocks. There are 7 blocks left in the box. How many blocks did Jie use?

 _____ blocks

b. Deon has 11 blocks. Andrea has 5 fewer blocks than Deon. How many blocks does Andrea have?

 _____ blocks

c. A large box of blocks is 13 dollars. That is 6 dollars more than a small box of blocks. How much is a small box of blocks?

 _____ dollars

d. Some blocks are on the table. Hunter takes 4 blocks. There are 2 blocks left. How many blocks were on the table before?

 _____ blocks

Step Ahead

Color the ⬭ beside the word problem that matches this equation.

$$12 - 7 = 5$$

○ A box holds 15 blocks. Monique takes out 7 blocks. How many blocks are left?

○ There are 12 blocks. Carter uses 5 blocks. How many are left?

○ A large box of blocks holds 12 blocks. A small box holds 7 blocks. What is the difference in the number of blocks?

Step In   Look at these 3D objects.

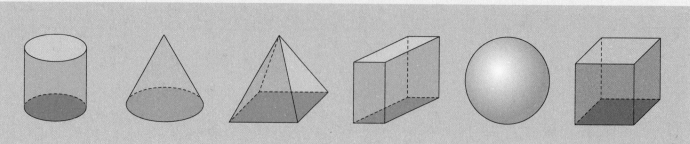

What 2D shapes were used to make these objects?

What other things do you
know about these objects?

Step Up   1.   Your teacher will give you a 3D object.
              Draw your object.

2.   Write the names of **two** other things that look like your object.

a. _____

b. _____

3.   My object has [   ] surfaces.

4. Color the ⬭ beside each statement that describes your object.

a.
- ⬭ It can roll.
- ⬭ It can stack.
- ⬭ It cannot roll or stack.

b.
- ⬭ It has all flat surfaces.
- ⬭ It has no flat surfaces.
- ⬭ It has some flat surfaces and some curved surfaces.

5. Draw each flat surface of your object.

Step Ahead Look at this 3D object.

a. How many surfaces does this object have?

b. What shape is each surface?

© ORIGO Education

Computation Practice   What bed does a mermaid sleep in?

★ Complete the equations.
★ Use a ruler to draw a straight line to join matching totals. Each line will pass through a letter.
★ Write the letter above its matching total at the bottom of the page.

$9 + 4 = \boxed{}$ ▶

◀ $\boxed{} = 1 + 9$

$8 + 2 = \boxed{}$ ▶

◀ $\boxed{} = 9 + 3$

$1 + 7 = \boxed{}$ ▶

◀ $\boxed{} = 5 + 9$

$7 + 5 = \boxed{}$ ▶

◀ $\boxed{} = 8 + 5$

$4 + 2 = \boxed{}$ ▶

◀ $\boxed{} = 2 + 6$

$8 + 6 = \boxed{}$ ▶

◀ $\boxed{} = 1 + 5$

$6 + 1 = \boxed{}$ ▶

◀ $\boxed{} = 5 + 2$

$\boxed{}$	$\boxed{}$ $\boxed{}$ $\boxed{}$	$\boxed{}$ $\boxed{}$ $\boxed{}$
10	7 6 8	13 12 14

ORIGO Stepping Stones • Grade 1 • 10.10

© ORIGO Education

Ongoing Practice

1. Use a ruler to draw one or two straight sides to complete three triangles.

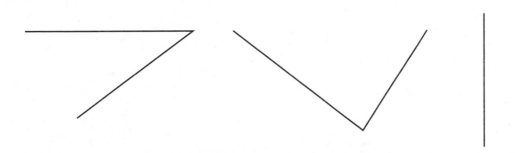

2. Color the ○ beside each statement that describes the object.

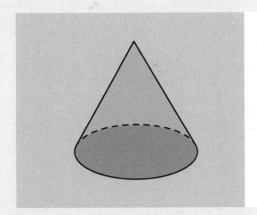

○ It can roll.

○ It has one flat surface and one curved surface.

○ It cannot roll or stack.

○ It has no flat surfaces.

Preparing for Module 11

Color coins to show the amount on each price tag.

a.

 6 cents

b.

 13 cents

Step In   Look at these two objects.

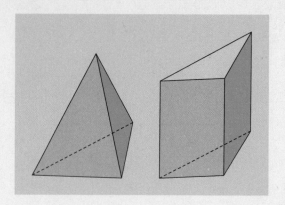

What 2D shapes were used
to make these objects?

What is the same about these two objects?

What is different about the two objects?

> Both objects have only flat surfaces.
> One object was made with triangles,
> and the other with triangles and
> non-square rectangles.

Step Up

I. Look at these pictures. Use real objects to help you
answer the questions.

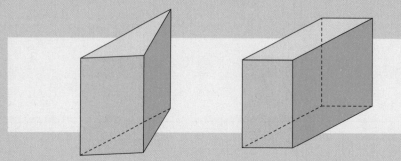

a. How are the objects the same?

b. How are the objects different?

2. Look at these pictures. Answer the questions.

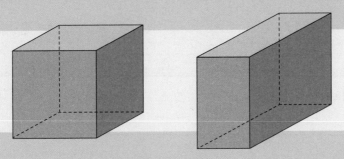

a. How are the objects the same?

_____

_____

b. How are the objects different?

_____

_____

Step Ahead   Read all the clues. Circle the object that matches.

Clues
- I have six surfaces.
- I can be stacked.
- Only one of my surfaces is curved.

Step In Look at this building.

Which 3D objects can you see?

Think about the buildings
in your neighborhood.
Which 3D objects can you see
in those buildings?

Think about blocks you have used at home or at school.
Which blocks do you use the most? Why?

Step Up 1. Count how many of each object has been used to
make each stack. The objects may be different sizes.
Write the number of each object below.

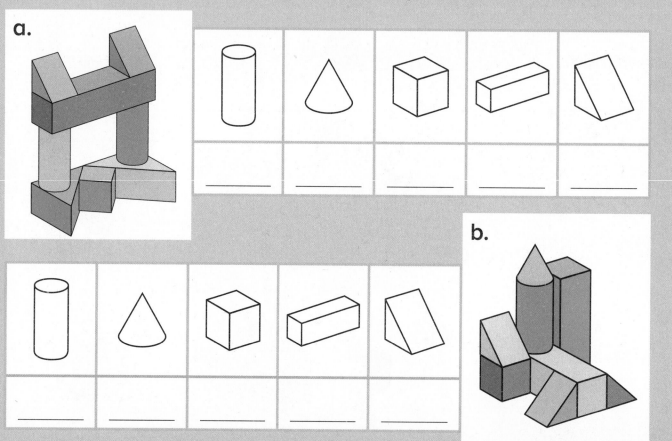

a.

b.

2. Circle the stacks below that can be made with these numbers of objects. The objects may be different sizes.

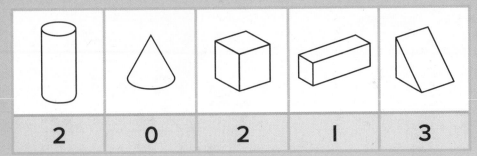

| 2 | 0 | 2 | 1 | 3 |

a.

b.

c.

d.

e.

f.

Step Ahead

Two of the stacks below match this stack.
One stack below does not match.
Circle the stack that does **not** match.

Think and Solve

a. Use a different color to show each pair of numbers that **add to 10**.

8	5	7	6	3	2	5

b. Circle the leftover number.

c. Use the number you circled to complete this equation.

☐ + ☐ = 10

d. Write a pair of numbers that are not shown above to complete this equation.

☐ + ☐ = 10

Words at Work

Write two sentences about these **3D objects**. You can use words from the list to help you.

_____

_____

_____

_____

_____

_____

_____

_____

cube
curved
surface
flat
edge
cylinder
same
different

Ongoing Practice

1. Draw two rectangles that look different.

FROM 1.4.11

2. Read all the clues. Circle the object that matches.

FROM 1.10.11

Clues ➡
- I have four surfaces.
- One surface is a rectangle.
- Only one of my surfaces is curved.

Preparing for Module 11

Draw coins to show the amount on the price tag. Then show the same amount in a different way.

12 cents

What is the difference between the number of books on each shelf?

Show how you know.

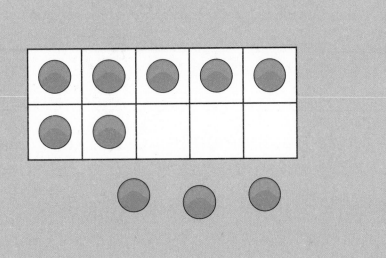

Chloe says she sees 7 + 3 = 10.

Marvin says he sees 10 − 3 = 7.

Who do you agree with? Showing your thinking.

Ask for feedback. Share how the feedback helps you.

Subtraction: Introducing the think-addition strategy (make-ten facts)

Step In   There were 16 stickers on this sheet.

STICKERS

Some of the stickers have been taken off.

How many stickers have been taken off the sheet?

How can you figure out the number of stickers that have been taken without counting each space?

Karen uses a number track to help her thinking.

| 1 | 2 | 3 | 4 | 5 | 6 | 7 | 8 | 9 | 10 | 11 | 12 | 13 | 14 | 15 | 16 |

What steps does she take?

Why does she make the first jump to 10?

What is the difference?

Karen uses addition to figure out the difference. She thinks 7 + ___ = 16.

Step Up   1.   Complete the equations. Draw jumps above the number track to show your thinking.

a.   15 – 9 = ☐

| 1 | 2 | 3 | 4 | 5 | 6 | 7 | 8 | 9 | 10 | 11 | 12 | 13 | 14 | 15 |

b.   13 – 8 = ☐

| 1 | 2 | 3 | 4 | 5 | 6 | 7 | 8 | 9 | 10 | 11 | 12 | 13 | 14 | 15 |

2. Figure out the number of dots that are covered.
Then complete the facts.

a.
$12 - 5 = \boxed{}$
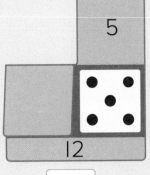
$5 + \boxed{} = 12$

b.
$14 - 9 = \boxed{}$
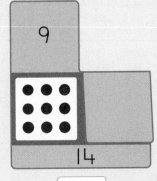
$9 + \boxed{} = 14$

c.
$12 - 8 = \boxed{}$
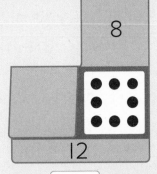
$8 + \boxed{} = 12$

d.
$14 - 8 = \boxed{}$
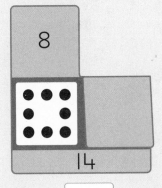
$8 + \boxed{} = 14$

e.
$13 - 5 = \boxed{}$
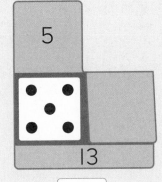
$5 + \boxed{} = 13$

f.
$15 - 6 = \boxed{}$
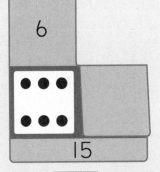
$6 + \boxed{} = 15$

Step Ahead

Complete the equations. Then circle the facts you solved by thinking about a double.

a. $17 - 8 = \boxed{}$

b. $14 - 6 = \boxed{}$

c. $14 - 5 = \boxed{}$

d. $15 - 8 = \boxed{}$

Step In There are 15 bees in total.

Some of the bees are flying around the hive. The rest of the bees are working inside the hive.

How many bees are working inside the hive?

Complete these facts to match.

$6 +$ ☐ $= 15$ $15 - 6 =$ ☐

Did you use addition or subtraction to figure out the answer?

What strategy would you use to figure out 13 − 8?

Step Up 1. Draw dots to figure out the missing part. Then complete the addition and subtraction facts to match.

a. 12 dots in total

$12 - 9 =$ ☐

think

$9 +$ ☐ $= 12$

b. 15 dots in total

$15 - 8 =$ ☐

think

$8 +$ ☐ $= 15$

2. Figure out the number of dots that are covered.
Then complete the facts.

a. 14 dots in total

14 – 5 = ☐

5 + ☐ = 14

b. 16 dots in total

16 – 9 = ☐

9 + ☐ = 16

c. 12 dots in total

12 – 7 = ☐

7 + ☐ = 12

d. 11 dots in total

11 – 4 = ☐

4 + ☐ = 11

e. 13 dots in total

13 – 9 = ☐

9 + ☐ = 13

f. 17 dots in total

17 – 9 = ☐

9 + ☐ = 17

3. Complete these facts.

a. 12 – 8 = ☐

b. 13 – 7 = ☐

c. 14 – 6 = ☐

d. 15 – 7 = ☐

e. 17 – 8 = ☐

f. 13 – 4 = ☐

Step Ahead   Write the missing numbers.

a. 14 – ☐ = 6

b. ☐ – 5 = 8

c. 15 – ☐ = 6

Computation Practice

Ramon was in the garden. He found something that had no legs and lots of teeth. What did he find?

★ Complete these equations. Then find each total in the puzzle below and color the matching letter.

10 + 27 = ☐	66 + 20 = ☐	10 + 19 = ☐
47 + 20 = ☐	10 + 51 = ☐	23 + 20 = ☐
20 + 55 = ☐	18 + 20 = ☐	10 + 64 = ☐
35 + 10 = ☐	10 + 42 = ☐	38 + 20 = ☐

1. Color some of the pictures. Then write the two subtraction facts to match.

a.

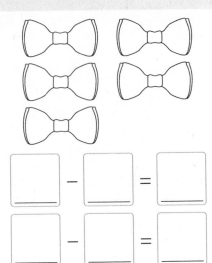

☐ – ☐ = ☐

☐ – ☐ = ☐

b.

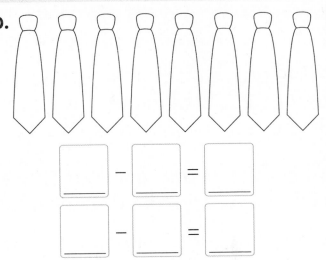

☐ – ☐ = ☐

☐ – ☐ = ☐

2. Complete these facts. Draw jumps above the number track to show your thinking.

a.

14 – 9 = ☐

| 1 | 2 | 3 | 4 | 5 | 6 | 7 | 8 | 9 | 10 | 11 | 12 | 13 | 14 | 15 |

b.

15 – 8 = ☐

| 1 | 2 | 3 | 4 | 5 | 6 | 7 | 8 | 9 | 10 | 11 | 12 | 13 | 14 | 15 |

Preparing for Module 12   Read each clue. Write the numeral to match.

a.   two ones
     five tens

b.   three tens
     zero ones

c.   seven ones
     zero tens

Step In There are 15 cars in a race.

Some of the drivers are male.
The rest of the drivers are female.

Write an equation to show how many
drivers could be male and female.
There is more than one equation.

$15 =$ ☐ $+$ ☐

15 cars start the race, but only 7 cars finish it.
How many cars did not finish the race?

Write an equation to figure out the number
of cars that did not finish the race.

What strategy did you use to find the answer?

I started at 7 and jumped to 10.
I then jumped from 10 to 15. I added
the jumps (3 + 5) to find the answer.

Step Up **I.** Write the answers. Then write
C, D, or **M** in each circle to
show the strategy you used
to figure out the answer.

Strategies

Ⓒ count-on
or -back

Ⓓ doubles

Ⓜ make-ten

◯ $7 - 2 =$ ☐   ◯ $8 + 4 =$ ☐

◯ $13 - 8 =$ ☐   ◯ $7 + 5 =$ ☐   ◯ $17 - 8 =$ ☐

◯ $7 + 9 =$ ☐   ◯ $11 - 2 =$ ☐   ◯ $12 - 3 =$ ☐

2. Write the answers on the race track.

start 9 − 3 = ☐   4 + 5 = ☐   9 + 3 = ☐

2 + 8 = ☐   12 − 4 = ☐   11 − 5 = ☐

8 + 7 = ☐   6 − 6 = ☐   4 + 7 = ☐

9 + 6 = ☐   8 − 0 = ☐   9 − 8 = ☐

3 + 5 = ☐   11 − 9 = ☐   finish

Step Ahead Write three different subtraction facts that each have a difference of 5.

a. ☐ − ☐ = 5   b. ☐ − ☐ = 5   c. ☐ − ☐ = 5

Step In   Julia collects trading cards.

The cards are put in a page of plastic sleeves and kept in a folder.

How many cards fit on each page?

Can you figure out the total without counting all the card spaces?

There are four cards in each row.
That is 4 + 4 + 4.

What subtraction fact could you write to show the cards that are missing on the page?

☐ – ☐ = ☐

Ang has the same pages for his cards. He has one page filled with cards, and one page with seven cards missing. How many cards does he have in total?

Step Up   1.   Solve each problem. Show your thinking.

a. Gloria has 3 packets of cards. Each packet has 6 cards. How many cards does she have in total?

_____ cards

b. Terri has 4 fewer cards than Reece. Terri has 9 cards. How many cards does Reece have?

_____ cards

2. Solve each problem. Show your thinking.

a. Rita has 6 more cards than Ben. He has 4 cards. How many cards does Rita have?

_____ cards

b. Lisa is given 7 fish cards. She now has 15 cards in total. How many cards did she have before?

_____ cards

c. Ruben has 11 cards. Some cards show fish and some show birds. How many cards might be in each group?

_____ fish _____ birds

d. Liam has 6 bird cards, 3 dog cards, and 4 fish cards. His friend has 10 cards. How many cards does Liam have in total?

_____ cards

Step Ahead Write your own word problem using each of these numbers. (14) (6) (8)

_____

_____

_____

_____

Think and Solve Write a number to make each balance picture true.

 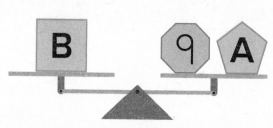

A =

B =

Words at Work

Zoe and Dwane each have some coins. Dwane has 4 cents more than Zoe. They have a total of 20 cents.

a. Draw a picture to show the coins each person could have.

b. Write about how you figured it out.

© ORIGO Education

Ongoing Practice

1. The number in the circle is the total. Write the missing number. Then write one addition fact and one subtraction fact to match.

a.

$\boxed{} + \boxed{6} = 8$

$\boxed{} - \boxed{} = \boxed{}$

b.

$\boxed{7} \quad \boxed{3}$

$\boxed{} + \boxed{} = \boxed{}$

$\boxed{} - \boxed{} = \boxed{}$

c.

$\boxed{5} \quad \boxed{4}$

$\boxed{} + \boxed{} = \boxed{}$

$\boxed{} - \boxed{} = \boxed{}$

2. Draw dots to figure out the missing part. Then complete the addition and subtraction facts to match.

a. 15 dots in total

15 – 9 = ____

think

9 + ____ = 15

b. 14 dots in total

14 – 8 = ____

think

8 + ____ = 14

Preparing for Module 12   Write the missing numbers on this track.

1		3				11				19
				8				16		
	5					14				

Step In   How many pairs of shoes do you see?

What is a quick way to figure out the total number of shoes?

Step Up   I.   Draw jumps of two. Color the numbers you land on.

a.

b.

2. Draw jumps of two. Color the numbers you land on.

a.

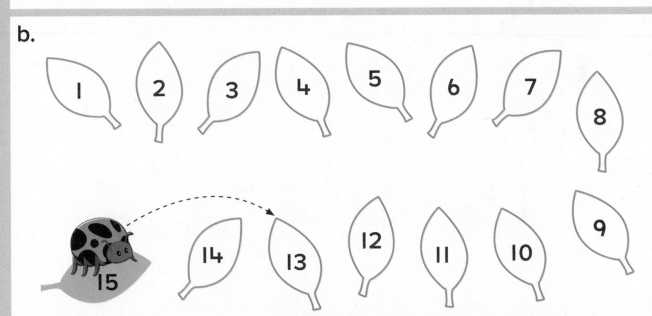

b.

Step Ahead These number patterns were made with jumps of two. Write the missing numbers.

a.

| 2 | 4 | | | 10 |

b.

| | 6 | | 10 | |

c.

| | 3 | | 7 | |

d.

| 3 | | | 9 | |

Step In   Look at the number track below.

How many fives can you find? Which numbers have a five?
How many zeros can you find? Which numbers have a zero?

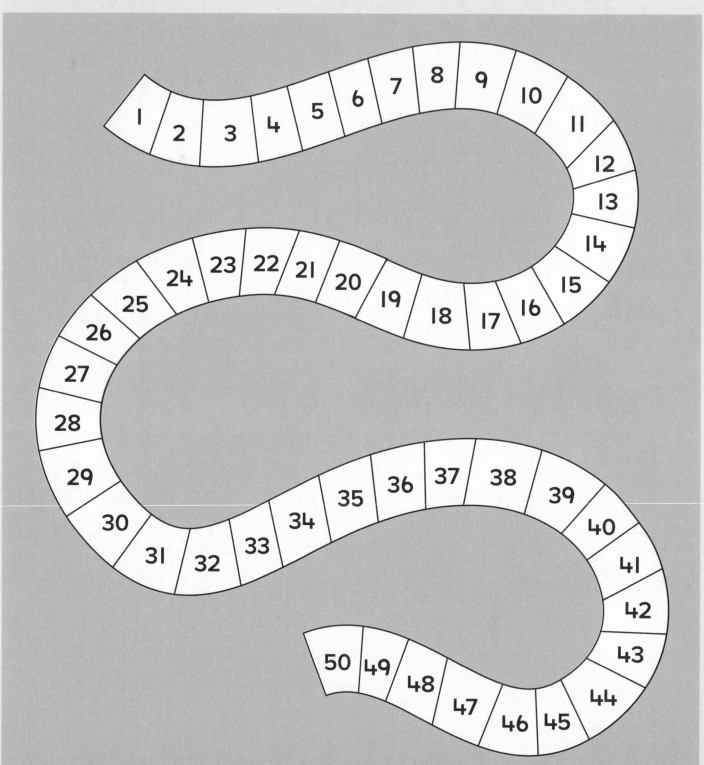

Use the number track on page 410 to help you complete these.

1. **a.** Start at 10. Draw ● on the numbers you say when you count by tens.

b. Write the numbers you say when you count by tens.

10				

c. Look at the numbers you wrote. Write about a pattern you see.

2. **a.** Start at 5. Draw ○ on the numbers you say when you count by fives.

b. Write the numbers you say when you count by fives.

c. Look at the numbers you wrote. Write about a pattern you see.

Step Ahead   Imagine the number track on page 410 went to 99.

a. Write the numbers you would say if you kept counting by tens.

50				

b. Write the numbers you would say if you kept counting by fives.

50									

Computation Practice

How is a baby like a basketball player?

★ Complete the equations. Then write each letter above its matching total at the bottom of the page.

$37 + 10 =$ ___ **i**	$56 + 10 =$ ___ **r**	$49 + 20 =$ ___ **a**
$39 + 20 =$ ___ **n**	$58 + 10 =$ ___ **w**	$25 + 10 =$ ___ **t**
$74 + 10 =$ ___ **b**	$23 + 10 =$ ___ **p**	$29 + 20 =$ ___ **e**
$66 + 20 =$ ___ **l**	$43 + 10 =$ ___ **h**	$55 + 20 =$ ___ **d**
$67 + 10 =$ ___ **y**		

Some letters appear more than once.

35	53	49	77	33	86	69	77

68	47	35	53	69	84	69	86	86

69	59	75	75	66	47	84	84	86	49

Ongoing Practice

I. Figure out the **difference** between each pair of cube trains. Then complete the equation.

a.

The difference is ☐

so 9 – 5 = ☐

b.

The difference is ☐

so 10 – 3 = ☐

2. Complete the equations. Then write **C**, **D**, or **M** in each circle to show the strategy you used to figure out the answer.

Strategies

Ⓒ count-on or -back

Ⓓ doubles

Ⓜ make-ten

◯ 9 – 2 = ☐

◯ 9 + 4 = ☐

◯ 14 – 8 = ☐

◯ 6 + 5 = ☐

◯ 17 – 9 = ☐

◯ 7 + 8 = ☐

◯ 11 – 3 = ☐

◯ 8 + 2 = ☐

Preparing for Module 12

Complete the equations. You can draw jumps above the number track to help you.

| 1 | 2 | 3 | 4 | 5 | 6 | 7 | 8 | 9 | 10 | 11 | 12 | 13 | 14 | 15 |

a. 5 – 2 = ☐

b. 3 – 1 = ☐

c. 9 – 2 = ☐

d. 12 – 3 = ☐

e. 8 – 3 = ☐

f. 15 – 2 = ☐

Step In This is a growing pattern. Draw the next picture.

Picture 1   Picture 2   Picture 3   Picture 4   Picture 5

How would you describe this pattern to another student?

This is a shrinking pattern. Draw the next picture.

Picture 1   Picture 2   Picture 3   Picture 4   Picture 5

What will the next picture look like? How do you know?

Look at this number pattern. Is this a growing or shrinking pattern?
How do you know?

| 1 | 3 | 5 | 7 | 9 | 11 | 13 |

What is a shrinking pattern that uses numbers?

Step Up I. Draw the next picture in this pattern.

Picture 1   Picture 2   Picture 3   Picture 4   Picture 5

2. Draw the missing picture in each pattern.

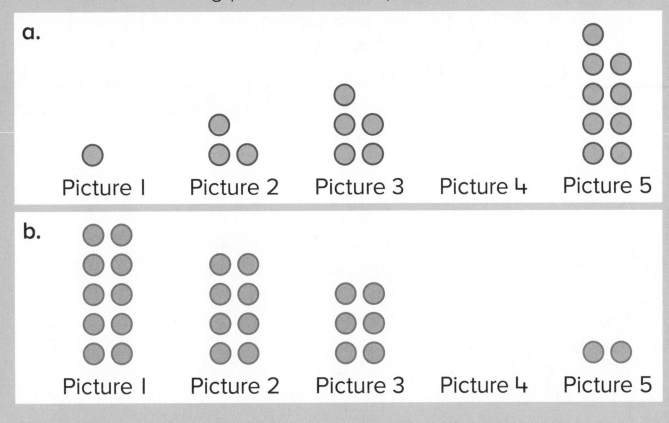

a.

Picture 1   Picture 2   Picture 3   Picture 4   Picture 5

b.

Picture 1   Picture 2   Picture 3   Picture 4   Picture 5

3. Write the missing numbers in each pattern.

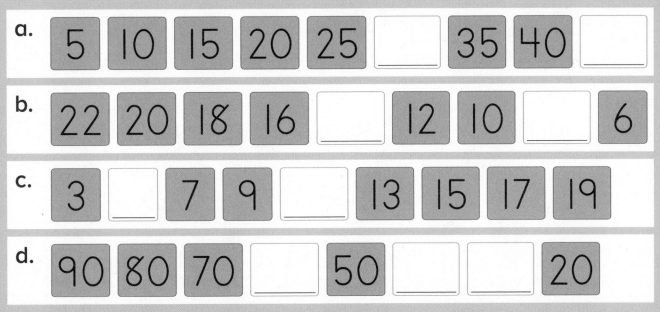

a. 5 10 15 20 25 ___ 35 40 ___

b. 22 20 18 16 ___ 12 10 ___ 6

c. 3 ___ 7 9 ___ 13 15 17 19

d. 90 80 70 ___ 50 ___ ___ 20

Step Ahead Write numbers to show a different **growing** number pattern.

Step In

How many dimes could you trade
for these pennies?

I can trade 10 pennies for 1 dime.

How many pennies could you trade for 3 dimes?
How do you know?

How many dimes could you trade for 50 pennies?
How do you know?

Step Up

1. Circle together the pennies you could trade for one
dime. Then write the number of pennies left over.

a.

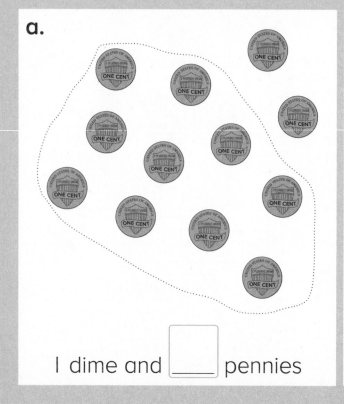

I dime and ____ pennies

b.

I dime and ____ pennies

2. Circle together the pennies you could trade for dimes. Then write the total number of dimes and pennies after the trade.

a.

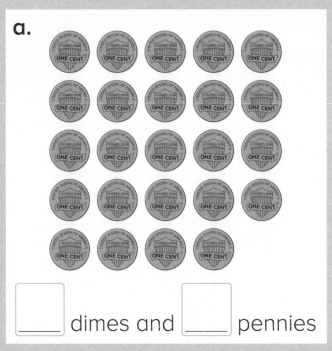

[____] dimes and [____] pennies

b.

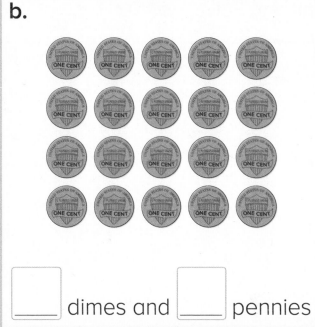

[____] dimes and [____] pennies

3. Write the number of pennies you could trade for these.

a. 9 dimes make the same amount as [____] pennies.

b. 7 dimes make the same amount as [____] pennies.

c. [____] pennies makes the same amount as 6 dimes and 7 pennies.

Step Ahead   Draw more coins to pay the **exact** amount for the toy.

50 cents

Think and Solve What is my lucky number?

- It is **greater** than 20.
- It is **less** than 30.
- It is a number you say when you start at 5 and **count by fives**.

Words at Work Choose and write a word from the list to complete each sentence below. Some words are used more than once. Some words are not used.

a.
If you start at 2 and _____ in steps

of _____ to ten, you will say 2, 4, 6, 8, 10.

b.
If you start at 10 and count in _____ of

_____ to fifty, you will say 10, 20, 30, 40, 50.

| five |
| count |
| ten |
| growing |
| steps |
| two |
| shrinking |
| repeating |

c. You will say the number 35, if you start at 5 and

_____ in steps of five.

d. The numbers 1, 2, 3, 4, 5, 6, 7 show a pattern that is

_____ by one.

e. The numbers 51, 41, 31, 21, 11 show a pattern that is

_____ by ten.

© ORIGO Education

1. Figure out how much **more** money is needed to pay the price. Draw jumps on the number track to show your thinking.

a.

| 4 | 5 | 6 | 7 | 8 | 9 | 10 | 11 | 12 | 13 | 14 |

Amount needed is _____ cents

b.

| 4 | 5 | 6 | 7 | 8 | 9 | 10 | 11 | 12 | 13 | 14 |

Amount needed is _____ cents

2. Write the missing numbers in each pattern.

a. | 15 | 20 | 25 | 30 | 35 | | 45 | |

b. | 90 | 80 | 70 | | | 40 | | 20 |

c. | 44 | 46 | 48 | | | 54 | 56 | 58 |

Preparing for Module 12

Complete each equation.
Cross out blocks to show your thinking.

a.

90 − 30 = ☐

b.

80 − 40 = ☐

Step In   **Look at these coins.**

What is the name of the small coin?
What is the name of the large coin?

How many pennies could you trade for one quarter?
How do you know?

How many nickels could you trade for one quarter?
How do you know?

One quarter is the same value as 25 cents, so that is 25 pennies.

How can you figure out the number of nickels you could trade for 2 quarters?

Step Up   1.   Circle together the nickels you could trade for 1 quarter. Then write the number of nickels left over.

a.

1 quarter and ____ nickels

b.

1 quarter and ____ nickels

2. Circle together the coins you could trade for quarters. Then write the total number of coins after the trade.

a.
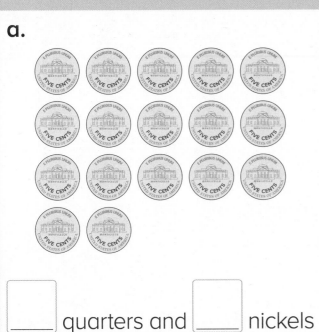

☐ quarters and ☐ nickels

b.
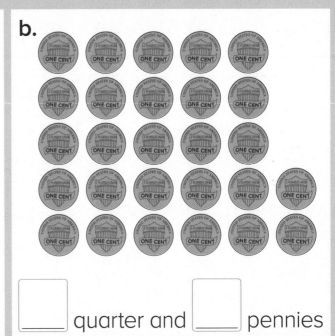

☐ quarter and ☐ pennies

3. Write the missing numbers.

a. 6 nickels make the same amount as ☐ pennies.

b. ☐ nickels make the same amount as 2 quarters.

c. 8 nickels make the same amount as ☐ dimes.

Step Ahead

Look at the collection of dimes. Then draw the nickels you could trade for the same amount.

dimes	nickels

Step In   Look at these pennies.

How many cents are there?
How do you know?

I counted by twos.
That is 10 cents.

How could you count these nickels to figure out the total value?

I counted by fives.
That is 60 cents.

How could you count these dimes to figure out the total value?

I counted by tens.
That is 80 cents.

Step Up   I.   Count by twos. Write the total amount.

_____ cents

2.   Count by fives. Write the total amount.

_____ cents

3. Use skip counting to figure out the total amount.

a.

[6 dimes, 2 nickels, 4 pennies]

_____ cents

b.

[2 dimes, 9 nickels, 2 pennies]

_____ cents

c.

[4 dimes, 5 nickels, 9 pennies]

_____ cents

Step Ahead Color coins to show 50 cents in two different ways.

Computation Practice

What is as big as an elephant but weighs nothing?

★ Complete these equations.

★ Write each letter in the box above its matching answer at the bottom of the page.

$22 + 20 =$ ___ **n** $29 + 1 =$ ___ **h** $6 - 2 =$ ___ **s**

$10 + 16 =$ ___ **o** $10 + 33 =$ ___ **e** $5 - 3 =$ ___ **a**

$16 + 20 =$ ___ **t** $8 - 3 =$ ___ **h** $8 - 1 =$ ___ **d**

$23 + 10 =$ ___ **p** $9 - 1 =$ ___ **a** $20 + 19 =$ ___ **w**

$10 + 39 =$ ___ **n** $20 + 28 =$ ___ **e** $9 - 3 =$ ___ **s**

$12 + 10 =$ ___ **l** $7 - 4 =$ ___ **a**

											'	
8	42		48	22	43	33	30	3	49	36		4

6	5	2	7	26	39

I. Color the ⬭ beside **each** statement that describes this 3D object.

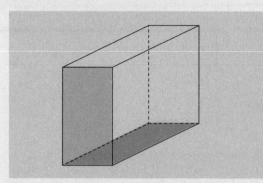

⬭ It can roll.

⬭ It can stack.

⬭ It has all flat surfaces.

⬭ It has two curved surfaces.

2. Circle together the coins you could trade for quarters. Then write the total number of coins after the trade.

[ ] quarters and [ ] nickels

Circle the glass that is holding **less** water.

a.

b.

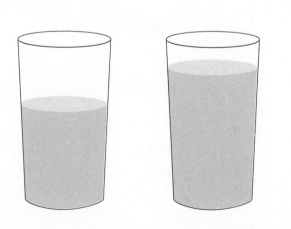

Step In

What coins could you use to pay the exact price for this item?

Paper Clips ○ 35 cents

What is the fewest number of coins you could use?
How do you know?

Could you use only dimes? Could you use only nickels?

What are some other ways you could pay for the item?

The symbol for cent is ¢.

Step Up

I. Color the coins you could use to pay the **exact** price for each item.

a.

○ 15¢

b.

○ 30¢

c.

○ 25¢

d.

○ 40¢

2. Cut out and paste the coins you could use to pay the **exact** amount for each item.

a.

b.

c.

d.

Step Ahead   Chayton used **five** coins to pay the exact price of this card. Cut out and paste the coins he used.

Step In   How many dimes could you trade for these pennies?

What is the name of this **bill**?
What is the value of this **bill**?

How many pennies could you trade for this bill? How do you know?

How many dimes could you trade for this bill? How do you know?

100 pennies can be traded for 1 dollar, so 10 dimes can be traded for 1 dollar.

The symbol for dollar is $.

Step Up   1.   Circle together the dimes you could trade for 1 dollar. Then write the total amount.

a.

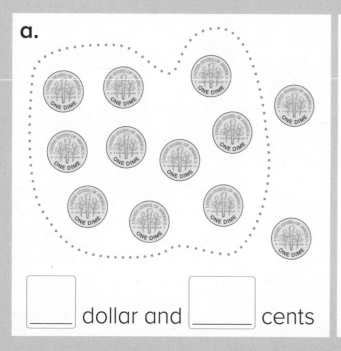

_____ dollar and _____ cents

b.

_____ dollar and _____ cents

© ORIGO Education

2. Circle together the coins you could trade for one dollar.
Then write the total amount.

a.

$____ and _____¢

b.

$____ and _____¢

c.

$____ and _____¢

d.

$____ and _____¢

3. Write these amounts as dollars and cents.

a. 126 cents is the same value as ____ dollar and _____ cents.

b. 105 cents is the same value as ____ dollar and _____ cents.

Step Ahead Color the purse that shows **exactly** one dollar.

| 9 pennies | 90 pennies | 90 pennies |
| 1 dime | 10 dimes | 1 dime |

© ORIGO Education

Think and Solve

Add the parts.

free $5 $5

$2 each $1 each

How much does this robot cost? $_____

Words at Work

Write the answer for each clue in the grid.
Use words from the list.

Clues Across

1. There are __ quarters in one dollar.

3. Two nickels have the same __ as one dime.

4. One dollar can be traded for 10 __.

Clues Down

1. __ nickels make one quarter.

2. 100 __ is the same value as one dollar.

five
cents
value
dollar
one
dimes
four
nickels

Ongoing Practice

I. a. What 2D shapes were used to make this 3D object?

FROM 1.10.10

b. How many surfaces does it have? ☐

2. Count by tens. Write the total amount.

FROM 1.11.10

a.

☐ cents

b.

☐ cents

Preparing for Module 12   Circle the toy that is **heavier**.

a.

b.

Lomasi finds five coins under a cushion on the couch. The total of the coins is 40 cents.

Which coins has Lomasi found?

Show how you know.

Eva and Brady are playing this game.

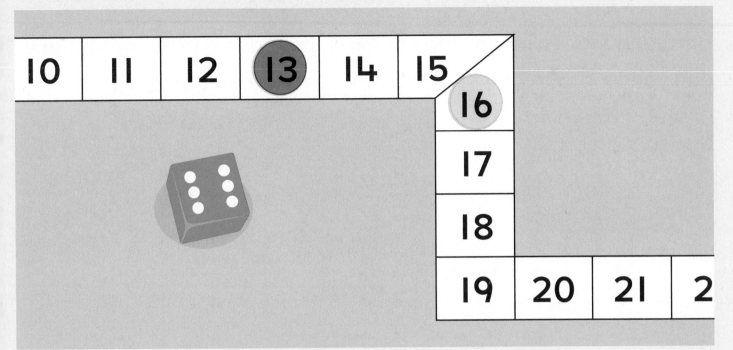

Eva says if she rolls a 6, she will be 3 spots ahead of Brady.

Do you agree with Eva? Show your thinking.

Ask for feedback. Share how the feedback helps you.

Step In Look at the hundred chart below.

Run your finger along all the numbers that have 6 in the ones place.

Run your finger along the numbers that have 6 in the tens place.

What do you notice?

1	2	3	4	5	6	7	8	9	10
11	12	13	14	15	16	17	18	19	20
21	22	23	24	25	26	27	28	29	30
31	32	33	34	35	36	37	38	39	40
41	42	43	44	45	46	47	48	49	50
51	52	53	54	55	56	57	58	59	60
61	62	63	64	65	66	67	68	69	70
71	72	73	74	75	76	77	78	79	80
81	82	83	84	85	86	87	88	89	90
91	92	93	94	95	96	97	98	99	100

Color any two numbers on the hundred chart.

What digits are written in the tens place and the ones place?

Which of your numbers is greater?

Are your numbers greater than 50? How do you know?

Use the hundred chart on page 434 to help you complete these.

1. Read the clue then write the matching number.

a. I have 2 in the tens place and 5 in the ones place.

◻

b. I have four ones and three tens.

◻

c. I have 9 in the ones place and 2 in the tens place.

◻

2. **a.** Write all the numbers that have an 8 in the **tens** place.

◻ ◻ ◻ ◻ ◻ ◻ ◻ ◻ ◻ ◻

b. What do you notice about these numbers on the chart?

◻

3. **a.** Write all the numbers that have an 8 in the **ones** place.

◻ ◻ ◻ ◻ ◻ ◻ ◻ ◻ ◻ ◻

b. What do you notice about these numbers on the chart?

◻

Step Ahead

a. Look at the hundred chart on page 434. Write all the **two-digit** numerals that have the same digit in the tens and ones places.

◻ ◻ ◻ ◻ ◻ ◻ ◻ ◻ ◻

b. What pattern do you see?

◻

Step In Color three numbers greater than 10 on this hundred chart.

Each number should be in a different row.

1	2	3	4	5	6	7	8	9	10
11	12	13	14	15	16	17	18	19	20
21	22	23	24	25	26	27	28	29	30
31	32	33	34	35	36	37	38	39	40
41	42	43	44	45	46	47	48	49	50
51	52	53	54	55	56	57	58	59	60
61	62	63	64	65	66	67	68	69	70
71	72	73	74	75	76	77	78	79	80
81	82	83	84	85	86	87	88	89	90
91	92	93	94	95	96	97	98	99	100

What things do you know about your numbers?

Which number has the greatest number of ones?

Which number has the greatest number of tens?

Which number is the greatest?

Which number is the least?

How many numbers are greater than 40?

Use the hundred chart on page 436 to solve these number puzzles.

I. Read the clues. Write the matching two-digit number.

a. I have 7 in my tens place and 3 in my ones place. ☐

b. I am greater than 44 but less than 46. ☐

c. I am between 33 and 39. You say me when you start at 5 and count by fives. ☐

d. I am in the same row as 56. You say me when you start at 10 and count by tens. ☐

2. Write all the two-digit numbers that match these clues.

a. I am less than 43 and I have 4 tens.

☐ ☐ ☐

b. I am greater than 69 and have 8 in the ones place.

☐ ☐ ☐

c. I am greater than 84. You say me when you start at 50 and count by fives.

☐ ☐ ☐

d. I have the same number of tens and ones. I am between 40 and 70.

☐ ☐ ☐

Step Ahead

Choose and write one number greater than 10. Write clues about your number. ☐

Computation Practice **What do you call a baby whale?**

★ Complete the equations.

★ Write each letter in the box above its matching total at the bottom of the page.

7 + 5 = ☐ a   8 + 9 = ☐ t

3 + 4 = ☐ i   5 + 3 = ☐ i

9 + 11 = ☐ u   6 + 5 = ☐ l

8 + 7 = ☐ t   2 + 4 = ☐ s

6 + 8 = ☐ l   7 + 6 = ☐ r

6 + 4 = ☐ e   3 + 1 = ☐ t

7 + 9 = ☐ q

☐	☐	☐	☐	☐	☐
12	14	8	4	17	11	10

☐	☐	☐	☐	☐	☐
6	16	20	7	13	15

1. Figure out the number of dots that are covered. Then complete the facts.

a.
12 − 7 = ☐

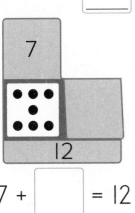

7

12

7 + ☐ = 12

b.
15 − 9 = ☐

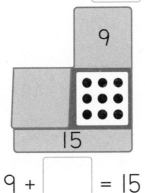

9

15

9 + ☐ = 15

c.
13 − 8 = ☐

8

13

8 + ☐ = 13

2. Think about the numbers on a hundred chart. Read each clue then write the matching numeral.

a. I have 3 ones and 5 tens.

☐

b. I have 7 in the tens place and 2 in the ones place.

☐

c. I have 4 tens and zero ones.

☐

Preparing for Next Year

Compare the numbers in the charts. Circle the words that are true.

a.

Tens	Ones
8	1

is greater than

is less than

Tens	Ones
1	8

b.

Tens	Ones
7	6

is greater than

is less than

Tens	Ones
8	3

Step In   Look at this number chart.

61	62	63	64	65	66	67	68	69	70

Start at 70. Count on in steps of 10. What numbers do you say?
Where will you write these numbers on the chart? How do you know?
Write the numbers on the chart.

Think about the numbers that come just before the numbers you wrote.
What digit will be in the ones place of each number? How do you know?
Write these numbers on the chart.

Start at 70. Count on in steps of 5.
Write these numbers on the chart.
What digit will be in the ones place of each number **just after**?
How do you know? Write these numbers on the chart.

Start at 70. Count on in steps of 2.
Write these numbers on the chart.
What digit will be in the ones place of each number **just before**?
How do you know?

1. Complete the chart on page 440.

2. Write the number that comes **just before** each of these.

a. [____] 120   b. [____] 105   c. [____] 119

3. Write the number that comes **just after** each of these.

a. 117 [____]   b. 110 [____]   c. 108 [____]

4. Write the numbers missing from these number chart pieces.

a. | 111 | | | |
   |---|---|---|---|

b. | | 107 | | |
   |---|---|---|---|

c. | 112 | | | | 116 | | | 119 | |
   |---|---|---|---|---|---|---|---|---|

Step Ahead   **a.** Circle in blue the numbers you say when you start at 100 and count on in steps of 5.

b. Circle in red the numbers you say when you start at 100 and count on in steps of 2.

102	110	105	120	115	118

c. Write what you notice about the numbers that are circled in both red and blue. What are two other numbers you would circle with both colors?

_____

_____

Step In **Look at this part of a number track.**

| 50 | 51 | 52 | 53 | 54 | 55 | 56 | 57 | 58 | 59 | 60 | 61 |

Imagine you were standing on 58 and made one jump back to 56. How can you show your jump on the number track?

You could draw an arrow like this.

| 50 | 51 | 52 | 53 | 54 | 55 | 56 | 57 | 58 | 59 | 60 | 61 |

What equation could you write to show what you did?

☐ – ☐ = ☐

What other jumps could you make on this part of the number track? What equations could you write to show what you did?

Step Up 1. Complete the equations.

| 27 | 28 | 29 | 30 | 31 | 32 | 33 | 34 | 35 | 36 | 37 |

a. $29 - 1 = $ ☐

b. $34 - 1 = $ ☐

c. $36 - 1 = $ ☐

2. Complete the equations. Draw jumps on the number track to help you.

| 51 | 52 | 53 | 54 | 55 | 56 | 57 | 58 | 59 | 60 | 61 |

a. 54 – 2 = ☐

b. 57 – 2 = ☐

c. 61 – 3 = ☐

| 74 | 75 | 76 | 77 | 78 | 79 | 80 | 81 | 82 | 83 | 84 |

d. 75 – 1 = ☐

e. 78 – 2 = ☐

f. 82 – 3 = ☐

| 88 | 89 | 90 | 91 | 92 | 93 | 94 | 95 | 96 | 97 | 98 |

g. 91 – 3 = ☐

h. 95 – 3 = ☐

i. 98 – 2 = ☐

3. Write the missing numbers.

a. ☐ – 2 = 65

b. ☐ – 1 = 47

c. ☐ – 3 = 71

Step Ahead Use a number track above to help you solve this problem.

Selena has 95 cents.

Jamar has 2 cents less than Selena

Ruth has 3 cents less than Jamar.

Connor has one cent more than Ruth.

How much money does Connor have?

 ☐ cents

Think and Solve

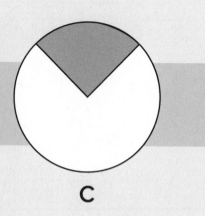

A   B   C

a. Which circle is one-half purple? ☐

b. Which circle is **less** than one-half purple? ☐

c. Which circle is **more** than one-half purple? ☐

Words at Work

Write clues to match the number **85**.
You can use words from the list to help you.

count by
tens place
ones place
number
less than
greater than
starts with
ends with

Ongoing Practice

1. Figure out the number of dots that are covered. Then complete the facts.

a. 14 dots in total

14 – 9 = ☐

9 + ☐ = 14

b. 13 dots in total

13 – 5 = ☐

5 + ☐ = 13

c. 15 dots in total

15 – 8 = ☐

8 + ☐ = 15

2. Figure out these number puzzles.

a. I am between 65 and 75. I have 2 ones.

☐

b. I am less than 20 but greater than 10. I have 7 ones.

☐

c. I have the same number of tens and ones. I am between 40 and 50.

☐

Preparing for Next Year

Circle the number. Then write the number of ones that are not circled.

a. Circle 60 fingers.

☐ not circled

b. Circle 20 fingers.

☐ not circled

Step In   Look at these numbers.

1	2	3	4	5	6	7	8	9	10
11	12	13	14	15	16	17	18	19	20
21	22	23	24	25	26	27	28	29	30
31	32	33	34	35	36	37	38	39	40
41	42	43	44	45	46	47	48	49	50

What number is 2 less than 45? How do you know?

What number is 1 less than 38? How do you know?

What is different about all the numbers that have 4 in the ones place?

Step Up   1.   Write the missing numbers.

a.

5 – 1 =

15 – 1 =

25 – 1 =

35 – 1 =

45 – 1 =

95 – 1 =

b.

18 – 2 =

28 – 2 =

38 – 2 =

48 – 2 =

78 – 2 =

88 – 2 =

c.

4 – 3 =

14 – 3 =

24 – 3 =

34 – 3 =

64 – 3 =

84 – 3 =

2. Think about the numbers **between I and 50**.

a. Write all the numbers that have 6 in the ones place.

b. Write the numbers that are **2 less** than the numbers you wrote.

3. Think about the numbers **between 50 and 100**.

a. Write all the numbers that have 9 in the ones place.

b. Write the numbers that are **2 less** than the numbers you wrote.

4. Write numbers **between II and 50** to complete these to show different equations.

a.

☐ − 3 = ☐

b.

☐ − 2 = ☐

c.

☐ − I = ☐

Step Ahead

Dorothy had 65 cents. She spent 3 cents. Vishaya had 66 cents. She lost 2 cents. Jacob had 67 cents. He gave away 3 cents.

Who had the least money left over?
Write equations to show your thinking.

☐

Step In   Look at this part of a hundred chart.

How can you figure out what number is behind the shaded tile?

I would start at 44 and count back in steps of 10 to the shaded tile.

				33		
41	42	43	44	45	46	

How many steps of 10 is that?

What equation could you write to match?

☐ – ☐ = ☐

What other way could you subtract numbers like these?

Step Up   1. Complete the equations. You can draw arrows on this part of a hundred chart to help.

1	2	3	4	5	6	7	8	9	10
11	12	13	14	15	16	17	18	19	20
21	22	23	24	25	26	27	28	29	30
31	32	33	34	35	36	37	38	39	40
41	42	43	44	45	46	47	48	49	50
51	52	53	54	55	56	57	58	59	60

a. $34 - 10 = $ ☐

b. $41 - 30 = $ ☐

c. $59 - 50 = $ ☐

2. Complete the equations. Use this chart to help.

41	42	43	44	45	46	47	48	49	50
51	52	53	54	55	56	57	58	59	60
61	62	63	64	65	66	67	68	69	70
71	72	73	74	75	76	77	78	79	80
81	82	83	84	85	86	87	88	89	90
91	92	93	94	95	96	97	98	99	100

a. $73 - 20 = \boxed{}$

b. $94 - 40 = \boxed{}$

c. $85 - 30 = \boxed{}$

d. $94 - 10 = \boxed{}$

e. $78 - 30 = \boxed{}$

f. $61 - 20 = \boxed{}$

3. Figure out and write each difference.

a. $52 - 50 = \boxed{}$

b. $33 - 20 = \boxed{}$

c. $88 - 30 = \boxed{}$

d. $99 - 60 = \boxed{}$

e. $67 - 30 = \boxed{}$

f. $56 - 20 = \boxed{}$

Step Ahead Write **+10**, **+20**, **−10**, or **−20** to make the number trails true.

a. $25 \rightarrow \boxed{} \rightarrow 45 \rightarrow \boxed{} \rightarrow 35 \rightarrow \boxed{} \rightarrow 55$

b. $74 \rightarrow \boxed{} \rightarrow 64 \rightarrow \boxed{} \rightarrow 74 \rightarrow \boxed{} \rightarrow 54$

Computation Practice

★ Complete the equations as fast as you can.

start

9 – 2 = ☐

8 – 4 = ☐

10 – 8 = ☐

8 – 7 = ☐

9 – 6 = ☐

6 – 4 = ☐

5 – 3 = ☐

7 – 5 = ☐

6 – 0 = ☐

10 – 3 = ☐

9 – 5 = ☐

7 – 1 = ☐

8 – 6 = ☐

5 – 2 = ☐

7 – 4 = ☐

9 – 1 = ☐

7 – 2 = ☐

10 – 4 = ☐

4 – 3 = ☐

9 – 0 = ☐

finish

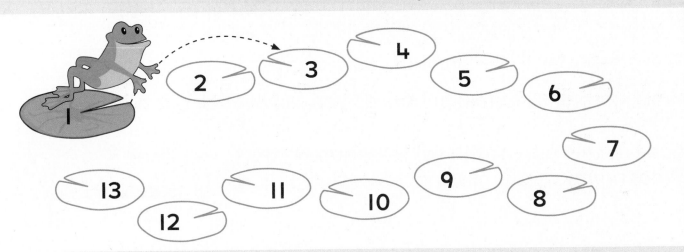
Ongoing Practice

1. Draw jumps of two.
Color the numbers you land on.

2. Write the answers. Use the number track to help you.

FROM 1.12.4

| 61 | 62 | 63 | 64 | 65 | 66 | 67 | 68 | 69 | 70 | 71 |

a. 63 – 2 = ☐

b. 68 – 1 = ☐

c. 65 – 3 = ☐

d. 70 – 2 = ☐

e. 69 – 3 = ☐

f. 71 – 2 = ☐

Preparing for Next Year

Color blocks to match the number shown on each expander.

a.

b.

Step In   Look at this part of a hundred chart.

1	2	3	4	5	6	7	8	9	10
11	12	13	14	15	16	17	18	19	20

What happens to the numbers as you move from right to left?

What happens to the numbers as you move back a row?

Look at this part of the same hundred chart.
What numbers are missing? How do you know?

Look at this piece of the hundred chart.
What numbers could you write in the white spaces?
How do you know?

Step Up   **1.** Complete the equations. Use the chart to help.

a.
43 – 2 =

b.
37 – 10 =

c.
25 – 3 =

21	22	23	24	25	26	27	28	29	30
31	32	33	34	35	36	37	38	39	40
41	42	43	44	45	46	47	48	49	50
51	52	53	54	55	56	57	58	59	60

d.
29 – 20 =

e.
53 – 1 =

f.
51 – 30 =

2. Figure out and write the answers.

a.
72 – 10 =

b.
65 – 2 =

c.
58 – 20 =

d.
47 – 3 =

e.
76 – 20 =

f.
43 – 1 =

g.
85 – 10 =

h.
35 – 1 =

i.
57 – 2 =

j.
96 – 10 =

k.
39 – 10 =

l.
69 – 20 =

Step Ahead Write the missing numbers along the trail.

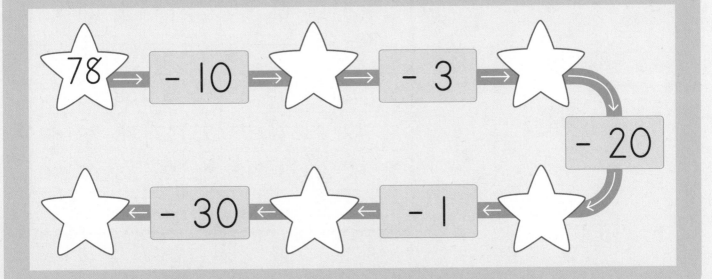

78 → – 10 → ☆ → – 3 → ☆ → – 20 → ☆
☆ ← – 30 ← ☆ ← – 1 ← ☆

Step In

Look at this part of a hundred chart.

How would you move the counter to subtract 20?

How would you move the counter to subtract 1?

How would you move the counter to subtract 21?

Does it matter if you subtract the ones before the tens?

1	2	3	4	5	6
11	12	13	14	15	16
21	22	23	24	25	26
31	32	33	34	35	36
41	42	(43)	44	45	46

Step Up

1. Draw arrows on this hundred chart to show how you figure out each equation. Then write the answers.

a. 36 − 12 = ____

b. 89 − 21 = ____

c. 75 − 31 = ____

d. 34 − 13 = ____

e. 49 − 33 = ____

f. 64 − 12 = ____

g. 27 − 21 = ____

h. 95 − 32 = ____

1	2	3	4	5	6	7	8	9	10
11	12	13	14	15	16	17	18	19	20
21	22	23	24	25	26	27	28	29	30
31	32	33	34	35	36	37	38	39	40
41	42	43	44	45	46	47	48	49	50
51	52	53	54	55	56	57	58	59	60
61	62	63	64	65	66	67	68	69	70
71	72	73	74	75	76	77	78	79	80
81	82	83	84	85	86	87	88	89	90
91	92	93	94	95	96	97	98	99	100

2. Write the number at the end of each part of hundred chart. Then complete the matching equation.

a.

65

$\underline{65} - \underline{22} = \underline{}$

b.

46

$\underline{} - \underline{} = \underline{}$

c.

82

$\underline{} - \underline{} = \underline{}$

d.

97

$\underline{} - \underline{} = \underline{}$

Step Ahead

This is part of a hundred chart. Write the numbers that should be shown in the white boxes.

					37			
	42							
51								
							68	

© ORIGO Education

Think and Solve Write a number to make each balance picture true.

A = _____

B = _____

Words at Work

What is **subtraction**? You can use words from the list to help you.

| less |
| equals |
| take away |
| count back |
| walk away |
| left over |
| subtract |
| count on |
| difference |

I. Draw the missing picture in each pattern.

a.

Picture I   Picture 2   Picture 3   Picture 4   Picture 5

b.

Picture I   Picture 2   Picture 3   Picture 4   Picture 5

2. Write the differences. You can use this chart to help.

a. $84 - 30 = \boxed{}$

b. $76 - 2 = \boxed{}$

c. $98 - 40 = \boxed{}$

d. $87 - 3 = \boxed{}$

51	52	53	54	55	56	57	58	59	60
61	62	63	64	65	66	67	68	69	70
71	72	73	74	75	76	77	78	79	80
81	82	83	84	85	86	87	88	89	90
91	92	93	94	95	96	97	98	99	100

Preparing for Next Year

Look at the blocks. Write the matching number on the expander. Then complete the number name.

hundreds

_____ hundred _____

Step In

Each of these bottles is full of water. Which bottle holds the most water?

How could you order these bottles by the amount of water that they each hold?

Two of these water bottles have the same **capacity**.

Capacity tells the amount of liquid that a container can hold.

Step Up

1. Circle the containers that would hold **less** water than this pitcher.

MILK

2. Circle the container with the **greater** capacity.
Circle both containers if the capacity looks the **same**.

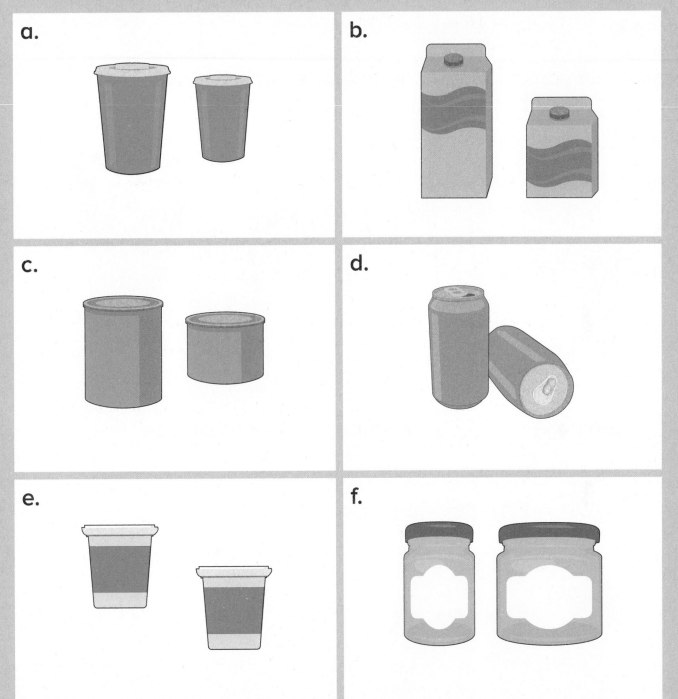

a.

b.

c.

d.

e.

f.

Step Ahead

This bottle has been squashed.
Has the amount of water that
the bottle can hold changed?
Share your thinking with another student.

© ORIGO Education

Step In   Look at these containers.

How could you use the scoop to figure out the capacity of each container on the table?

How could you record the results?

What else could you use to measure the capacity of each container?

Step Up   **1.** Write the number of scoops for each container.

Container	Number of Scoops of Rice	
a.		_____ scoops
b.		_____ scoops
c.		_____ scoops
d.		_____ scoops

2. Write the number of scoops for these containers.

a. _____ scoops

b. _____ scoops

c. _____ scoops

3. Compare these containers from Questions 1 and 2.
For each pair, circle the container that can hold more.

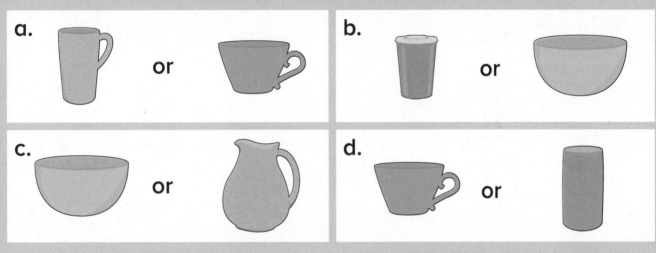

a. ☐ or ☐

b. ☐ or ☐

c. ☐ or ☐

d. ☐ or ☐

Step Ahead   Look at the containers in Questions 1 and 2.

a.
Color the ⬭ beside the number of 🥄 it would take to fill two 🥤.

  ⬭ 5   ⬭ 8   ⬭ 6   ⬭ 10

b.
Color the ⬭ beside the number of 🥄 it would take to fill two 🥣.

  ⬭ 2   ⬭ 6   ⬭ 5   ⬭ 3

Computation Practice   **What is the best way to catch a fish?**

★ Complete the equations. Then write each letter above its matching answer at the bottom of the page. Some letters appear more than once.

$32 - 3 =$ ____   **h** $77 - 2 =$ ____   **i**

$23 - 2 =$ ____   **u** $65 - 1 =$ ____   **s**

$47 - 1 =$ ____   **m** $55 - 3 =$ ____   **v**

$51 - 3 =$ ____   **o** $91 - 2 =$ ____   **a**

$84 - 2 =$ ____   **y** $88 - 1 =$ ____   **n**

$29 - 1 =$ ____   **w** $44 - 3 =$ ____   **e**

$66 - 3 =$ ____   **r** $41 - 2 =$ ____   **t**

29	89	52	41	64	48	46	41	48	87	41

39	29	63	48	28	75	39	39	48	82	48	21

1. Circle together the pennies you could trade for dimes. Then write the total number of dimes and pennies after the trade.

FROM 1.11.8

[   ] dime and [   ] pennies

2. Write the number of scoops of rice for each container. Then circle the container that holds the most.

FROM 1.12.10

Container	Number of Scoops of Rice	
a.		[ ] scoops
b.		[ ] scoops
c.		[ ] scoops

Preparing for Next Year   Figure out the total. Write the addition fact.

a.   7

[   ] + [   ] = [   ]

b.   8

[   ] + [   ] = [   ]

Step In | What do you know about the mass of each grocery item in this picture?

How could you compare the mass of the bread and the oats?

Write **bread** and **oats** on this pan balance to show your thinking.

The bread and cereal have the same mass. The oats are heavier than the cereal.

Step Up | **1.** Look at each picture. Write **more** or **less** to complete each sentence.

a.

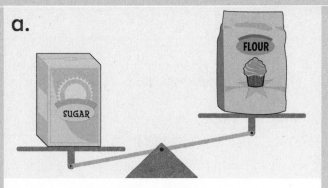

The sugar weighs _____ than the flour.

b.

The noodles weigh _____ than the cheese.

2. Look at each picture. Write **more than**, **the same as**, or **less than** to compare the mass.

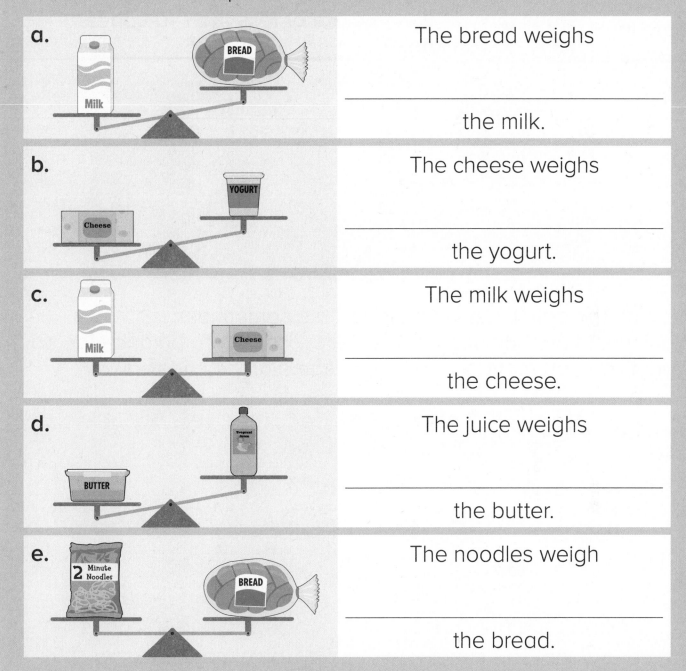

a. The bread weighs _____ the milk.

b. The cheese weighs _____ the yogurt.

c. The milk weighs _____ the cheese.

d. The juice weighs _____ the butter.

e. The noodles weigh _____ the bread.

Step Ahead

Look at the balance pictures above. Write **yogurt** and **milk** on this pan balance to make it true.

Step In

Does the ball weigh more or less than 10 cubes?
How do you know?

Imagine the ball and the cubes had the same mass.
What would the balance look like? How could you balance the ball?
Would you add more cubes or take some of the cubes away?

Step Up

1. Look at the balance. Color the ⬭ beside the words that best describe the mass of the toy.

a.

- ◯ more than 12 cubes
- ◯ fewer than 12 cubes
- ◯ balances 12 cubes

b.

- ◯ more than 10 cubes
- ◯ fewer than 10 cubes
- ◯ balances 10 cubes

c.

- ◯ more than 16 cubes
- ◯ fewer than 16 cubes
- ◯ balances 16 cubes

d.

- ◯ more than 9 cubes
- ◯ fewer than 9 cubes
- ◯ balances 9 cubes

2. Write the number of cubes in each space. Color the ⬭ beside the words that best describe the mass of the toy.

a.

- ◯ more than _____ cubes
- ◯ fewer than _____ cubes
- ◯ balances _____ cubes

b.

- ◯ more than _____ cubes
- ◯ fewer than _____ cubes
- ◯ balances _____ cubes

c.

- ◯ more than _____ cubes
- ◯ fewer than _____ cubes
- ◯ balances _____ cubes

d.

- ◯ more than _____ cubes
- ◯ fewer than _____ cubes
- ◯ balances _____ cubes

Step Ahead

How many cubes might this toy weigh?
Write three possible answers.

_____ cubes

_____ cubes

_____ cubes

Think and Solve Read the clues. Use the letters to answer.

Clues

G holds more than **D**.

E holds less than **D**.

F holds less than **E**.

a. Which cylinder holds the **most**? ☐

b. Which cylinder holds the **least**? ☐

Words at Work Choose and write words from the list to complete the sentences below. One word is not used.

| capacity |
| mass |
| heavier |
| holds less |
| lighter |
| holds more |

a. _____ tells the amount something weighs.

b. A small cup _____ than a milk bottle.

c. A pumpkin is _____ than a ones block.

d. A bathtub _____ than a cup.

e. _____ tells the amount a container can hold.

Ongoing Practice

I. Color the coins you would use to pay the **exact** amount for each item.

a.

30¢

b.

45¢

2. Write the number of cubes. Then color the ○ beside the words that best describe the mass of the piece of fruit.

a.

○ more than _____ cubes

○ fewer than _____ cubes

○ balances _____ cubes

b.

○ more than _____ cubes

○ fewer than _____ cubes

○ balances _____ cubes

Preparing for Next Year

Write the addition fact.
Then write the turnaround fact.

a.

8

_____ + _____ = _____

_____ + _____ = _____

b.

5

_____ + _____ = _____

_____ + _____ = _____

c.

3

_____ + _____ = _____

_____ + _____ = _____

My grandpa is 97 years old.

My dad is 30 years younger than my grandpa.

I am 30 years younger than my dad.

My brother is 3 years younger than me.

How old is my brother?

Show how you know.

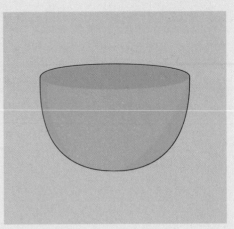

Kyle has 3 bowls of ice cream.

Brianna has one bowl of ice cream.

José has 2 bowls of ice cream.

Brianna says they all had about the same amount of ice cream.

Kyle says they did not have the same amount.

Who do you agree with?

 Ask for feedback. Share how the feedback helps you.

Associative property of addition

This property means that three or more numbers can be added in any order and the total will not change. For example, 6 + 6 + 4 = 6 + 4 + 6 = 18.

Capacity

The amount of liquid a container can hold.

Cent (¢)

Describes the value of one or more coins. For example, a penny has a value of one cent.

Column

An arrangement of numbers one above the other.

Column

Commutative property of addition

This property means that two numbers can be added in any order and the total will not change. For example, 3 + 5 = 8 and 5 + 3 = 8. These facts are commonly called turnaround facts.

Difference

The answer in a subtraction equation. For example, the equation 9 − 2 = 7 tells that the difference between 9 and 2 is 7.

Digit

The numerals 0 to 9, for example, the number 19 uses the digits 1 and 9.

Dollar ($)

A unit of money that can be traded for 10 dimes or 100 pennies.

Fact family

Describes two additon facts and two subtraction facts that use the same two parts and the same total, as shown.

$$4 + 2 = 6$$
$$2 + 4 = 6$$
$$6 - 4 = 2$$
$$6 - 2 = 4$$

Gate tally

The fifth mark in a group of 5 tally marks. This mark is drawn across the first 4 tallies, as shown.

Growing pattern

A pattern that gets bigger in each part. For example, in this pattern, each picture grows by one circle.

Picture 1   Picture 2   Picture 3   Picture 4

Half-past

Describes any time when the minute hand is pointing to 6 on an analog clock or the numbers to the right of the colon on a digital clock show 30. For example, if the minute hand is pointing to 6 and the hour hand is just after the 4, the time is half-past 4, or four thirty.

Hour

A unit of time that is the same as 60 minutes.

Hundreds

In the base-ten number system, the first place to the left of the tens place. The value of any digit in this place is described as a number of groups of one hundred. For example, in 237, the value of the 2 is 2 groups of one hundred.

Ones		
H	T	O
2	3	7

Liquid

A substance like water, milk, or soda.

Minute

A small unit of time. 60 minutes is the same time as one hour.

One hundred

The counting number just after 99.
This expander shows 100.

Ones place

In a number, the place that is just right of the tens place. The value of any digit in this place is described as a number of groups of one. For example, in the number 37, the value of the 7 is 7 groups of one.

Hundreds	Tens	Ones
	3	7

Regroup

To regroup 10 ones as 1 ten. For example, 6 tens and 13 ones is the same value as 7 tens and 3 ones.

Related facts

Two subtraction facts that use the same two parts and the same total. For example, $7 - 4 = 3$ and $7 - 3 = 4$.

Results

Data that has been collected then shown in a graph or table.

Roll

To move by turning over and over. For example, a sphere and cylinder can roll because they have a curved surface.

Row

An arrangement of numbers or objects placed side by side.

Row →

8	1	6
3	5	7
4	9	2

Shrinking pattern

A pattern that gets smaller in each part. For example:

Picture 1   Picture 2   Picture 3   Picture 4

STUDENT GLOSSARY

Skip counting

Counting forward or back by a number greater than one.
For example, 2, 4, 6, 8, and so on.

Stack

To put 3D objects on top of each other to make a tower.

Surface

The outside of a 3D object. The surface of an object may be curved or flat.

Tally chart

A table with tally marks to show a set of data.

Place	Tally	Total
Gym	卌 卌 卌 卌 III	23
Playground	卌 卌 III	13

Tally mark

A symbol used to record the number of times something occurs.

four tally marks

Tens

In the base-ten number system, the first place to the left of the ones place. The value of any digit in this place is described as a number of groups of one ten. For example, in 56, the value of the 5 is 5 groups of one ten.

	Ones	
H	T	O
	5	6

Weigh

To measure the mass of something.